Praise for *The Bc*

As a physician, I have over tr
the woeful inadequacy in the treatment of back pain. The
psychotherapeutic approach to this vast problem has been
much neglected and to this end Tom Barber's book
represents a major breakthrough and "sea change" in
approach. Over the years, Tom has used his abundant
therapeutic skills to the benefit of so many patients. This
work is a culmination of his endeavour, one that will I am
sure give great relief to the legions of back pain sufferers.

Dr Osmond Jones, Medical Doctor – London

Tom Barber writes as he speaks, with clarity and
sensitivity; connecting theory and practice in language that
can be easily understood not just by professionals, but also
the lay person. He explains the workings of the mind, and
the connection between the mind and body, with pertinent
personal and professional anecdotes and experiences,
using analogies, metaphors and suggestions. He teaches
the reader techniques for relief of pain by using various
holistic and systemic strategies, such as ·Mindfulness,
Neuro-Linguistic Programming, including TOTE, Self-
Hypnosis and the Emotional Freedom Technique.

I have been a sufferer of neck and back pain for many
years, and I have found Tom's *The Book on Back Pain*
amazing. Following the techniques and strategies he
teaches stage by stage, I am now better armed with new
knowledge and confidence that the process really and truly
works! Thank you, Tom.

Latha Kanthaswamy, Nurse and Therapist – London

Tom provides an empowering, practical and easily accessible guide for you to take charge, regain responsibility for your health and well-being, and gain freedom from your pain.

Alex Weitzel, VAI IIHHT IHBC CG, Sports and Holistic Practitioner – Essex

I really think this is a great book. Throughout my long experience as a professional masseur, I would say that a large percentage of my clients have an emotional issue underlying their back pain. A great many of them see chiropractors, osteopaths and physiotherapists, but I feel that Tom's great techniques would really help people with back problems, caused by specific injuries. I will definitely recommend these to my clients.

Floyd Matthews, ITEC IPTI, Remedial Masseur – London

This is an invaluable book aimed at helping people suffering with chronic back pain, which often plays a huge limiting part in people's lives. Tom Barber has distilled his vast knowledge of integrative therapy into ten easy chapters in *The Book on Back Pain*. He is a master when it comes to putting information in simple and yet effective ways. This book is engaging, easy to read and comprehend, and clearly enables the reader to understand and unravel this massive problem.

As a doctor, I have seen people struggling with the impact of chronic back pain who describe it feeling like a big black cloud, hindering them in moving forward with full efficiency. This well written book will definitely help in empowering people to take the control back. I am glad that this book is available, as it has huge potential to make a positive difference to individuals through its unique approach. Well recommended!

Dr Amit Kumar, Medical Doctor – Kent

THE BOOK ON BACK PAIN

THE ULTIMATE GUIDE TO <u>PERMANENT</u> RELIEF™

TOM BARBER, M.A., D.Hp.

PUBLISHING

The Book on Back Pain: The Ultimate Guide to Permanent Relief™

First Edition, published by 10-10-10 Publishing.

Copyright © 2013 Tom Barber.

The right of Tom Barber to be identified as the author of this work has been asserted by him in accordance with the Copyright, Designs and Patents Act 1988.

The information contained in this book is not intended to replace the services of a trained health professional. You are advised to consult with your health care professional with regard to matters relating to your health, and in particular regarding matters that may require diagnosis or medical attention. Hypnosis, hypnotherapy, guided imagery and self-hypnotic techniques are not in any way meant as a substitute for standard medical, psychological or psychiatric treatment for serious or life-threatening conditions, such as medical trauma, surgical emergencies, bacterial infections, certain bodily "mechanical" difficulties, and thought disorders such as psychosis or schizophrenia. The techniques in this book are offered as an adjunct to self-healing, self-help, and behavioural modification. The intent of the author is purely to offer information of a psychological nature to help in your quest for relief from pain. If you are unsure whether to use this book, seek advice. Neither the author nor the publisher shall be liable for any loss, injury, or damage arising from any of the information contained herein, or use of any method, technique or suggestion contained in this book.

The author is not responsible for any of the websites contained within this book, or the content of those websites, unless that website and its content are exclusively owned by the author.

ISBN: 978-1-927677-38-4

Acknowledgements

Writing this book for me has been an absolute joy. To convey the methods and techniques in this book to as many people as possible that need to know about the power of the mind, is an exciting prospect. Yet I couldn't have done this alone. I would like to extend my heartfelt thanks to Raymond Aaron and his incredibly powerful author programme. The desire to write this book was made infinitely easier with Raymond's meticulously detailed advice. An intrinsic part of the success of this project has been due to my "book architect" Lori Murphy, whose support has continually kept me on my toes and spurred me on. This steadfast support of course would not amount to anything unless the project got completed, and so I owe a tremendous thank you to Sandra Westland for her first editing of the book and the input of her therapeutic ideas and suggestions, which enormously improved and enhanced the book. Sandra's support is always truly inspirational. My thanks go to Osmond Jones, Latha Kanthaswamy, Alex Weitzel, Floyd Matthews, and Amit Kumar, for their support and advice in reviewing the book. I would like to thank John Harten for his sublime editing skills. I knew from our first correspondence that I was in good hands. I would also like to thank Tony Loton for his technical expertise, and patience, in the formatting of the book.

When I first started this project, I wondered how I would convey my message through the written word alone, and decided early on to use a variety of visual images to help contextualise the methods I was writing about. To that end I would also like to extend my thanks to Clara at Azurextwilight Design for her ability to understand what I was asking for in my image descriptions, and her unique artistic expertise in bringing them to life, and giving the book a visual story. My thanks also go to Marie Littlewort for her inspirational artistic skill in designing the book cover.

Finally, and I think most importantly, I owe a huge debt of gratitude to my past and current students for their unwavering belief in the methods I teach, and their embracement and advancement of them. Without them, this project would not have been possible.

This book is dedicated to my dear Mum,
Patricia June Barber,
who sadly passed away this year, 2013.
I will miss her more than I even yet know,
but am also deeply thankful that she is now at peace,
and no longer in pain.

For you, Mum.

Contents

Table of Figures...xiii

Foreword...xv

Chapter 1—Introduction: Getting Ready for the Ultimate Relief...1

Chapter 2—Step 1: Pain and Mindfulness.........................15

Chapter 3—Step 2: Your Ultimate Outcome.......................29

Chapter 4—Step 3: Deconstructing Your Experience of Pain..41

Chapter 5—Step 4: Reframe for the Ultimate Gain..........51

Chapter 6—Step 5: The Headquarters 63

Chapter 7—Step 6: Handing It Over to You.......................77

Chapter 8—Step 7: Pain Still There!...................................85

Chapter 9—Step 8: Emotional Freedom Technique.........97

Chapter 10—Conclusion...109

Resources...115

References..117

Index...121

Table of Figures

1:1 Wong-Baker FACES™ Pain Rating Scale.......................4

1:2 0-10 Numerical Pain Intensity Scale................................4

1:3 Melzack and Wall's Gate Control Theory of Pain 11

2:1 Rubin's Vase..22

5:1 Submodalities Choice Indicator Scale 1.......................55

5:2 Submodalities Choice Indicator Scale 2.......................56

9:1 EFT Face and Body Points..98

9:2 EFT Face and Body Points Descriptions – From Right to Left..106

Foreword

The Book on Back Pain: *The Ultimate Guide to Permanent Relief* by Tom Barber is intended to help you gain something that you have been longing for … relief from your back pain and control of your life.

By learning how powerful your mind is and embracing its awesome possibilities and potential, you really can change your life for the better and gain freedom from your pain. Tom's vast knowledge and experience is superbly captured in this book as he takes you through a comprehensively structured programme. He explores the mind-body connection and then teaches you techniques that succinctly show you how to harmonize and maximize your mind-body potential for the ultimate relief you deserve.

This book will guide you to find out just how much power and control you can take for yourself in your pain relief and will make an unquestionable difference in how you feel every day from the moment you read the first chapter.

In this book:

- You will learn just how you work and what impacts your experience of pain. Your beliefs, values, and personal history are all inextricably linked and in need of unravelling.
- You will discover the power of your mind as you create for yourself the ultimate inner focus and the essential state of mental and physical relaxation needed for pain relief that will make the difference.
- You will connect with a variety of tried and tested techniques that have never been put together

before in this way. It builds into a powerful programme of self-care that you can control, grow and master for the rest of your life.

- You will become adept at finding a way that suits you in your quest for the ultimate relief of back pain and truly make it a reality.

You owe it to yourself to give this unique programme the chance to make a difference to your life and to help you with your ultimate pain relief. Why not become one of the many people who have completed this programme with Tom and who have reaped the benefits of using such powerful methods in this way too?

Raymond Aaron
New York Times Bestselling Author
www.MillionaireBusinessBootCamp.com

Chapter 1
Introduction
Getting Ready for the Ultimate Relief

It was a typical Sunday morning in my kitchen, and I was getting ready to head off to play rugby. It was my passion, and still is, although the years have crept up on me and I'm no twenty year old anymore, as I was then. I'd eaten my breakfast, changed into my sports kit and was about to head off when I sneezed and was swiftly introduced to agony! My introduction to back pain was as simple as that, and I'll never forget it. As I sneezed, I felt something in my lower back go "pop." In fact, I'm sure I heard it! I froze, as something deep inside me told me not to move, that something was wrong. I started to move around *very* slowly and with each step the searing pain in my back grew worse, and then the throbbing started and I knew then what back pain was all about. I knew something was wrong but didn't know what. Every position I tried to put myself into was pure agony, except that one position that everybody I've spoken with about back pain knows intimately: the foetal position. I started to move down onto all fours and it felt like someone was stamping on my back. The pain continued to sear throughout me as I slowly

1

scrunched my whole body up into the only position my instinct told me to move to and ... relief. I stayed there for a while.

Now - being only twenty years of age - I still had that sense of invincibility about me, and I decided in my wisdom that it was only a temporary pain and would actually wear off after a while and so I could just simply carry on step-by-step, so I made my way to my car. As I drove to the rugby club, the pain caused sweat to pour off me, but still I thought it would only last a while and, like all good rugby players chosen for the second or third-tier team, when I reached the club I self-medicated with a pint of real ale. It probably wasn't the best of ideas.

After applying copious amounts of heat spray and sinking another swift half-pint of ale, I stumbled onto the rugby field with my fellow teammates and the game began. Now, what I haven't mentioned is that my position in the rugby team was that of a hooker! As the first scrum down descended upon me, I put myself in the middle of the scrum pack with two six-foot guys, each weighing 210 lbs., either side of me, eager to obliterate all eight men in front of them. The referee blew his whistle and they pushed, and pushed, and pushed, and I screamed and screamed and screamed. Now I really knew something was wrong! As I left the field I decided that I probably needed to rest. Not even able to drive home, I called someone to come and get me, went home and for the rest of the day just sat, and stood, and walked around. Nothing seemed to get rid of the pain. So, knowing this was now serious, I phoned an emergency chiropractor who agreed to see me the very same day.

Introduction

When I arrived at his office and told him of my morning story, he just looked at me and shook his head. He then positioned me on his examination couch and began to manipulate my back, crunching me this way and the other. It was agony. He gave me some very helpful advice by telling me that my hips weren't formed correctly, that actually I had the hips of a woman, which were made for giving birth. I wasn't quite sure *how* that was helpful, but it's stayed with me.

Over the next few weeks I underwent a series of treatments and manipulations carried out on my back and gradually the pain subsided. It was in fact much better off from the very first treatment, even though the chiropractor told me that it might initially be more painful.

My experience over the following few years felt rather strange. In moments of stress, anxiety, worry and fear, just the ordinary usual ups and downs in the story of life, I began to experience a re-emergence of lower back pain. Indeed, when I became stressed or anxious or worried, it was like revisiting that very same day on the rugby pitch; that very same searing pain all came flooding back, and this I found rather confusing.

I hear this kind of story every day when working with people with back pain. In the Ultimate Relief pain workshops I run, I hear so many of these different accounts that show a distinct correlation between the pain people feel in their body and their emotional and psychological state. That's what this book is about: dealing with the connection between the pain you feel in your back and the emotional and psychological aspect of that pain. As you begin to take control of your back with your mind, your mind will become stronger, and as your mind gets

3

stronger, your back responds. We will in effect be creating in these chapters a new way of living - new neural pathways. A new kind of mind-body connection that your back is crying out for. So let's start in the now, because as you move through this book chapter by chapter we want to see your back improving. That's the aim. The Ultimate Relief is our goal, but we will only be sure of the changes that are happening when we can measure them.

The 0 to 10 of Pain Measurement – How Intense Is It?

So, to start, I want you to rate your experience of your back pain. There are many ways of doing this. You can use the Wong-Baker FACES™ Pain Rating Scale (2001) below:

Figure 1:1 Wong-Baker FACES™ Pain Rating Scale

Or you can use a simple numerical scale, such as the one below, to rate the intensity of the pain. You choose what fits for you.

PAIN SCORE 0-10 NUMERICAL RATING SCALE

Figure 1:2 0-10 Numerical Pain Intensity Scale

Introduction

The main thing is that you have a way of gauging where your back pain is now on the intensity scale, and thus what will have changed and how much less you experience that pain as we move through this book.

So, to rate it now, complete the following sentence:

"Presently my intensity rating of pain is _____."

We're going to revisit this at the end of each chapter, so you'll see the progress you're making.

Can Your Mind Really Overcome Pain?

This is a question that I am asked all the time in my work. Yet what seems plain is that our mind is overcoming pain a lot of the time. Think about situations in sport, where during a game a player sustains an injury yet keeps playing, sometimes mostly unaware that they have injured themselves.

I've personally run the London marathon, twice, in 2010 and 2012. I know how the body can switch off pain. During the marathon, I suffered from cramp, runners stitch, incredibly sore toes and discovered and felt muscles I didn't realise I had. Yet there is something amazing that the body does during times like this, where pain can be seemingly "overridden." What impacts this, however, are four different factors that contribute to your experience of pain.

The 4 Factors of Pain

These are:

1. *Your emotional connections to pain*

The pain in your back travels along two pathways from the source of your pain in your back, to your brain. One of these is the sensory pathway, which transmits the physical sensation, and the other is the emotional pathway, which goes from the pain source to the amygdala and the anterior cingulate cortex. These are the areas of the brain that process emotion. In my experience, pain from illness, disease and chronic conditions include an anxiety and depression which is inseparable from the physical sensations of pain. Your emotions are part of your experience of pain and the perpetual cycle.

In my work as a psychotherapist I see many clients suffering from back pain, and the vast majority suffer from feelings of anxiety and depression. The cycle of pain *is* a depressing one. The more pain you feel, the gloomier you become. The more down you feel; the more pain you experience. It's a vicious, relentless cycle which perpetuates until it's broken, or maybe you are. This miserable situation is what brought me to writing this book. The first step often is to recognise this vicious cycle. Then using the methods you will learn in the following chapters, we can go about addressing what's happening in both your body *and* mind.

2. *Your past experiences of pain*

Your current experience of pain can be affected by earlier life experiences of pain felt long ago. How you were reacted to within your family in times of pain, and also different cultural styles, affect how you respond to pain in adult life and your attitude to potential pain experiences. Only the other day, one of my young grandchildren fell off his pushbike while we were out in the back yard. He fell, looked up and around, and only when his eyes met mine, which were filled with worry, did he start crying. Children often look to their parents for cues on how to react when they fall or hurt themselves. Often, the more serious the injury the more distressed the parent, and the louder the child then cries.

In some families though, pain is seen in a different way. Expectations of being strong and tough, means that a child might grow up more resilient to pain, and this follows them through into adult life. Pain, then, is a subjective experience. What the very word pain elicits is a quite personal matter. It stands to reason that your past experiences of pain not only affect your current experience of pain, but what you expect pain to feel like in the future.

3. *Your characteristics*

People with low motivation or poor self-esteem can often perceive a pain stimulus as more severe. They seem to have a lower pain threshold and, as they are already under strain and feeling anxiety, they feel any additional stress distinctly. Somebody who is adventurous, optimistic and confident will certainly experience pain differently to somebody who is anxious, pessimistic and introspective.

4. *Your perceptions of what pain means*

Finally, what pain means has an impact on how you experience it. A paper cut, for example, hasn't the same meaning as a deep gash near an artery. Even though we know how painful a paper cut can be, it just doesn't signify the same level of seriousness, and hence the pain is not felt as severely. Some people view pain as something in need of attending to, while others seem to live with pain in a much more unconcerned way. Each of them *experience* the pain, but have different ideas as to what pain means.

Take some time now to look at these four dynamics. Where do you think you have been influenced in the past in these areas? How are they impacting your experience of pain? Use the table below to record your thoughts.

The 4 factors of pain	Where do they come from?	How do they impact me?
1. Your emotional connections to pain		
2. Your past experiences of pain		
3. Your characteristics		
4. Your perceptions of what pain means		

Introduction

What Is Pain?

Simply put, pain is a physical sensation that causes bodily suffering and distress. It is also an emotional experience associated with actual or potential tissue damage. As we will see later on in the book, emotional pain, such as sadness, anger, or fear, can be stored away in the body and is just as real as the pain felt from a physical injury. Pain protects us and motivates us to withdraw from potentially damaging situations, to protect a damaged body part while it heals, and to avoid those and similar situations in the future, whether they be physical or emotional.

Pain can be incredibly useful! Acute pain is often unexpected, such as that experienced in an accident. It's often intense and short-lived, but can also lead to anxiety and fear of further pain or injury. I recall a training session when I was playing rugby. We were practicing what we called "set plays," replicating what we would do in particular situations during match time. I can recall distinctly the moment where I chased the ball, stepped down to grab hold of it and then - bang - a fellow team member tackled me - hard - as he was supposed to. Unfortunately for me, it was an icy January night in the UK, and the ground was solid. As I was twisted around, my whole body turned, but the studs of my rugby boot remained firmly in the ground, keeping my foot heading in one direction and the remainder of my body facing the other. It was the first time I can remember as a grown man, screaming like a baby! The sound of my ligaments snapping was only equalled by the collective grimacing sounds of my teammates. They each knew that sound was a year out of the game. This was *acute* pain, and the recovery included much anxiety and fear as I slowly regained the ability to walk and eventually run. Generally though, when this kind of injury heals, the pain goes away.

Chronic pain, however, is more likely the kind of pain you're experiencing if you're reading this book. You may not have had an injury to your back as serious as the one I've just described of my ankle, but over time, the pain has slowly gotten worse, almost creeping up on you, until it gets to the point where you can take no more or simply cannot live with it. Chronic pain has often been around for a while, and various treatments aren't working or working little at best. It's this kind of chronic pain that this book is designed for. I'm going to show you how you can become the "boss" of your back again.

The Dual Carriageway of Pain - The Gate Control Theory

Melzack and Wall introduced their "gate control" theory of pain in the 1965 *Science* article "Pain Mechanisms: A New Theory," which describes how the transmission of pain signals could be intercepted in the dorsal horn within the spine, the area that consists of the sensory fibres responsible for regulating and modulating the incoming impulses of pain, so that a "gate" could be closed and the signal of pain could be switched off.

Nerves from all over your body run to the spinal cord, which is the first main meeting point for the nervous system. In the spinal cord, you can imagine a series of gates through which messages about pain arrive from all over your body. These gates can sometimes be much more open than at other times. This is important because it is through these gates that messages from your body pass towards your brain. If the gates are more open, then more pain messages pass through to the brain and you are likely

Introduction

to experience a high level of pain. If the gates are more closed, then fewer messages get through and you are likely to experience less pain.

Ordinarily, through our bodily experiences, our large nerve fibres are delivering messages of our sensations through the dorsal horn in the spinal cord, synapsing onto the transmission cells, which then make their way up the spinothalamic tract to the brain. So, ordinarily, the gate is closed and no pain is experienced. What happens during an injury, however, is that our smaller nerve fibres pass impulses through the gate, opening it and allowing the pain signal to move to the transmission cells, which then passes pain to be registered in the brain.

The diagram below (*figure 1:3*) indicates how the use of hypnotic suggestion can directly influence the closing of the gate, so that the messages of pain can't get through.

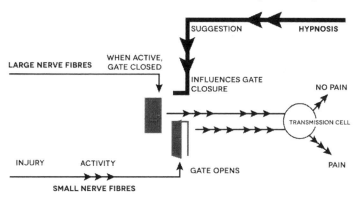

Figure 1:3 Melzack and Wall's Gate Control Theory of Pain

Imagine for a moment now the electrical impulses carrying the messages of pain from your back, making their way through your spine and through the dorsal horn of your spine, at which point they come across this gating mechanism. Imagine now *slamming* the gate shut, so as the message hits the gate it's stopped in its tracks, and the electrical impulses just disperse and fade away. This simple visualisation helps you imagine this process taking place, but using it whilst in the state of hypnosis connects your powerful inner mind to actually making these changes happen.

Bonus Number 1 - The Power of Hypnosis

In Chapter 6 you will be learning how to use self-hypnosis, and exactly how to influence these messages to take control of your back pain. But I don't want you to wait that long! So, here for you now is my special Bonus Number One! So you can start learning about hypnosis and how it can help you make powerful changes, alongside this book I am giving you my Free eBook on Hypnosis and NLP. To download your copy now, simply go to www.TomBarberMedia.com.

In the next chapter you are going to learn how to shift your mind into the correct state for change to take place, but the more you find out about *how* your mind and you operate, the more control you can take over you, your life and your back pain. Enjoy learning!

How to Use This Book

A lot of books you may have read invite you to dip in and out of each chapter and find what works for you. This isn't one of them. In writing this book I have taken each of the methods you are about to learn and put them in an organised sequential order. There is a logical and practical reason for this. If you were to start reading Chapter 6 now, it likely wouldn't make sense, as each of the chapters builds on the previous chapters' learning. Each chapter will address your back pain in a different way, and they have been organised through many years of teaching these methods, and finding the order in which they work best.

I'm going to hazard a guess that the first ever time you rode on two wheels that it wasn't on a Harley Davidson. We start with what we can manage and build upwards. This book is the same. We are going to start with what your mind can manage and build up to the ultimate relief. So, take each chapter step by step, and only when you've completed each chapter, move on to the next one.

Chapter 2
Step 1: Pain and Mindfulness
From Pain to Peace ... Can It Happen?

Why Get Mindful?

The first thing here is to explain what "mindfulness" means. The idea is certainly not a new one. According to the teachings of the Buddha (circa 500 BCE), mindfulness is considered to be one of the seven factors on the path to enlightenment. So what is it? Well, plainly speaking, mindfulness is a state of purposeful being in which one can pay attention to the reality of one's experience.

Consider how often you try to get through your day and turn your attention away from the pain in your back. As hard as you try, it still niggles away, doesn't it? There may be times where you become distracted by something that grabs your attention; a surprise telephone call from an old friend, a funny joke that makes you cry with laughter, an emergency you need to deal with, but, hovering around in the background, the pain remains, wearing you down.

Well, imagine if you were to spend a specific period of your day focussing on nothing but your back pain. How would that feel to you right now? It may well sound counterintuitive at first. "Why would I want to focus entirely on my back pain when I'm trying to get rid of it?", you may ask.

The answer is in taking control. Becoming mindful of what you are experiencing in your back is the first step to taking control of your body, using both your mind and body and the power of focussed attention. As Alexander Wynne, in *The Origin of Buddhist Meditation* (2007), wrote, "A key innovative teaching of the Buddha was that meditative stabilisation must be combined with liberating discernment." (p. 73), and this is what leads to the healing power of wisdom.

Psychology has embraced the use of mindfulness in recent years (Germer et al., 2005; Siegel, 2007; Shapiro and Carlson, 2009), and it has been noted to be effective in treating anxiety and depression, which is pertinent to the back pain sufferer. Focussing on emotion in particular, Fisher (2012) writes about mindfulness as a way of managing anger, which can be useful, as prolonged pain can become incredibly frustrating and has led many of the people I've worked with to feelings of anger and resentment. A study by Zautra et al. (2010) showed a decrease in the experience of pain when using mindful breathing exercises, as well as a decrease in these kinds of negative emotion. Cramer et al. (2012) write about mindfulness in the treatment of lower back pain in particular, and the prolific author Jon Kabat-Zinn also offers his highly acclaimed *Mindfulness for Pain Relief: Guided Practices for Reclaiming Your Body and Your Life* (2010).

Step 1: Pain and Mindfulness

The practice of mindfulness then, is an accepted and useful tool in the fields of psychology and psychotherapy, and offers much to help people slow down and take control of the pain they are experiencing.

Taking Control of Your Physical Presence

Many of the techniques you will learn in the following chapters begin from a place of mindfulness, and so this is a good place to start. Until now you may have tried varying different types of medication, or been given numerous exercise and stretching regimes to help relieve your back pain, and, if you are unlucky enough to have suffered from back pain for many years, may well have simply been told to "lay still on a flat surface for as long as you can each day." The treatment of back pain is certainly different now however, with movement the key to recovery. Indeed the famous author on back pain, John Sarno, advocated movement as a critical need in his bestselling book *Healing Back Pain: The Mind-Body Connection* (1991). But what about guiding your attention *into* the pain to ease it?

New Positions - Holding Yourself in a New Way

We are now going to use five different exercises to get you accustomed to mindfulness. Each one is different but all have the same purpose - to attune you to focussing on the reality of your experience of your back pain. Make sure you have around ten minutes of quiet time to spare and that you are somewhere where you'll be undisturbed. There's no rush. We spend a vast amount of time in this hectic life rushing around. Life is busy, and these exercises will be invaluable in helping you to slow down and become mindful. There's no success or failure with each technique, as what you experience will change over time. It often takes a long time simply to get to a short moment of mindful clarity, so it's helpful to make this part of your overall strategy in gaining the ultimate relief. All mindfulness techniques start here, so get as good as you can at each exercise before you move on to the next one.

Exercise 1: 60-Second Mindfulness

This is a simple mindfulness exercise which you can do anytime throughout the day. It helps to have some time on your own, but it only takes sixty seconds, so you should be able to do it anywhere and at any time. When you're settled and ready, check your clock or watch and make a note of the time. Then, for the next sixty seconds, your sole task is to focus all your attention on your breathing. It may seem like a long time, but that is all you have to do for sixty seconds. You don't have to close your eyes; just concentrate on your breathing to the exclusion of everything else. With each breath in, notice your stomach and chest rising, and with each breath out, notice them lowering.

You might notice your mind wandering off, which is normal when you first start. You might need to build it up from twenty seconds to thirty, forty and then eventually sixty seconds. Sixty seconds, however, is your goal. Once you have achieved that then you can make it longer, but start with just one minute as your target.

Exercise 2: Conscious Focussed Observation

When you've achieved one full minute of mindful attention, then we can build up your mindful "connection." In this exercise I want you to first find yourself somewhere quiet and again make sure you'll be undisturbed. Then pick up an object that you have lying around. Any object will do. It doesn't matter, as it's simply going to be a point of focus for you. Hold your chosen object in both of your hands and let your attention be fully absorbed by your object. Examine it, allowing your observations to move around it in different directions. You may find thoughts about it wandering into your mind, but there's no need to do anything with them. You don't have to assess your object, or think about it, or make sense of anything about it. Just observe your object for what it is and stay with your object as completely as you can. Let it become the central point of your world at this moment in time.

The goal is to experience a feeling of being in the now and present in your experiencing of life. When you become present in your life and can really be in the moment, then you stop your past experiences of pain, and your future expectations of pain taking over, leaving you present solely in the *now*. This conscious focussed observation brings the *present* wholly into your reality.

Exercise 3: Mindfulness Triggers

"Triggers" occur in all sorts of situations. Pavlov's dogs are a very well known example of how they can be used. Ivan Pavlov (1849-1936) conducted an experiment where he trained dogs to salivate on command. He presented dogs with a ringing bell followed by food. After repeating the same process a few times, the dogs, upon hearing a bell ring, would salivate, anticipating food, whether it appeared or not. The conditioned stimulus - the bell - created a conditioned response within the dogs, with them salivating at the prospect of being fed.

In this exercise we are going to use the same idea. You are going to train yourself to respond in a certain way whenever a certain trigger or cue occurs. Think now about a common trigger that happens from day to day. Let's take the telephone ringing. Your goal is that whenever you hear this sound, you focus on becoming mindful - of an object, or something more innate, like your breathing. Your breathing works well, as it's something you cannot escape. You are always breathing, hopefully! So, when the telephone rings, your task is to train yourself to mindfully shift your attention to your breathing, and specifically *each* breath in and *each* breath out.

Another common experience is looking in the mirror. Most of us do this every day, so it's a common experience that we can use to become mindful. When you look in the mirror, shift your attention to your breathing. You can look at yourself whilst you do it or close your eyes, whatever suits you. What other common life experience triggers can you think of? What do you do each day as a matter of course? What are the most repetitive experiences you have each day?

List five of them below now.

1.

2.

3.

4.

5.

Step 1: Pain and Mindfulness

From now on, in each of these situations, remember to shift into a mindful state of being. This mindfulness triggers exercise is an excellent way of moving you out the pain of the past and your expectations of future pain, and snapping you into the now, where you can think more clearly and really embrace the techniques you are about to learn, in a way that fits for you.

Exercise 4: Mindful Listening

"I just need some peace and quiet." Do you recall having said this before? Most of us crave for some peace at some point or another. Just some quiet time to sit and slow down, yet this isn't always easy. How many times have you stopped to have a break, just to rest and take some time out, where you then begin to think about all the things you could, or should, be doing! Sometimes it's like the noise from outside, and even our inner noise, just doesn't stop.

In training yourself to *use* these sounds to take you into a mindful state of awareness, you turn them from being a distraction, into a useful way of calming your mind and then taking control. How many sounds around you are you aware of right now? You might be sitting in your living room, on the train, in your lunch break at work, or in your favourite place. Wherever you are, you will likely be experiencing a variety of different sounds from your external surroundings; people chatting, the sound of a radio, traffic driving past, or a clock ticking. Most of these sounds fade into the background, while we focus on whatever we are doing at the time; what's most at the fore of our attention. One of the best ways of putting this into context I have found is through my studies in Gestalt psychology, which talks about "figure and ground." The most well-known visual example of figure-ground perception is the Rubin vase two dimensional image, that Danish psychologist and phenomenologist Edgar Rubin (1886 - 1951) presented:

Figure 2:1 Rubin's Vase

Through this visual image we can see a distinction between two pictures. On one hand we have a picture of a vase, and on the other the picture of two faces looking at each other. Can you see them both? Which image then is figure, and which is ground? Well, this changes as you focus on one of the pictures in particular. As you become aware now of the figure of the vase, the faces become ground, and when you bring the faces forward in your perception, the vase becomes ground. As you look at the image above, swap between them and see how this works.

Let's think about how you switch from your fore experience to your ground experience in relation to what you're *physically* aware of. I'm going to assume you are sitting down, or perhaps even lying down reading at the moment. So ... are you aware of the chair or bed beneath you? Well, you are now! Were you before I mentioned the chair or bed? Likely not! We moved you in focussing your attention onto the chair, or bed, so that it became the *fore* of your experiencing, which was previously the *ground*.

This happens because we cut out parts of our sensory experiences. It's impossible to be aware of all of our experiences at any one time, and really not very useful anyway. Imagine if from moment to moment you had to keep checking the chair was still beneath you every time you were sitting down! Nothing would ever get done, would it? Thankfully, we have the ability to shut parts of our reality out.

Let's get back to your "inner noise". Think about how many thoughts you have moving through your mind at any one time. We tend to work on the same premise with our thoughts as the fore-ground principle. Think about your thoughts right now. You're reading these words; you're concentrating on what I'm saying, and maybe you're questioning how *you* experience all of this - and what else is there? What am I having for my evening meal? Did I lock the front door? Or did I pay that bill, or take my pain medication? It's busy in there, isn't it?

So, this is one of the most important techniques I use with clients and students of the Ultimate Relief programme, as it helps you take charge of your inner noise though mindful listening. Not just what you are hearing from your external world, but what you are listening to from inside you too.

Listening Mindfully

You've taken sixty seconds to attune to your experiencing, practiced being mindfully focussed on a specific object, and also become aware of the triggers that will help you *become* mindful. Now you are going to listen mindfully. Let's put a time scale to it. For the next two minutes you're going to mindfully listen, to one sound in particular.

Take a few seconds now to notice one sound around you. It may be the sound of a clock ticking, or the birds outside, or a certain sound that is happening. It needs to be a sound that's going to remain constant for a while. Even the most disturbing of sounds can help us become mindful. I remember one from many years ago at the beginning of my career, sitting in my then office with a client. We were doing a session of hypnotherapy, where I was guiding them through a visualisation. I needed quiet! My client needed quiet! In the grounds of where I was working there was a small farm, and within that farm were two peacocks. I called them Sid and Cyril. Why? Because every afternoon around 4pm they would fly up onto my therapy room roof and start squealing what sounded like, "Sid … Cyril!" You could hear them from two streets away!

Life is like that: fire engines, police sirens, telephones, builders. Noise is everywhere. So I decided to use this sound mindfully … and said to my client … "and as you hear the sound of Sid and Cyril squealing, just focus on that, and focus on nothing else, just the sound of them communicating." My client drifted deeply into a wonderful state of relaxation simply because I didn't try to exclude the *reality* of their auditory experience, but instead got them to mindfully focus on it. It's a strange experience, really focussing on the sounds around us. We spend so much time trying to block things out that we miss the benefits of listening … mindfully.

So, whatever is happening around you right now, I want you to become mindful of the time and take two minutes to practice mindful listening. Whatever you become aware of, let it be your anchor. That's your sound. That's what you are going to focus on. It doesn't matter what it is; just let whatever grabs your attention be your focus. Now, stay with it for a whole two minutes. Let yourself be with your sound for a whole two minutes. Push away from your mind all else to the exclusion of that sound. Let it just be "you and here and now." I wonder if you are beginning to notice an inner stillness, a sense of peace and quiet, as many of my workshop participant's describe.

Exercise 5: Mindful Breathing

Becoming mindful is a step further than being conscious of your back pain. It's a real focussed attention on what makes your back pain what it is. Maurice Merleau Ponty (1908-1961), the French philosopher, once said, "We are first and foremost a body in the world." As an existentialist, he explored and wrote extensively about the body being an intrinsic aspect of our existence in the world. To be mindful of what you are experiencing not only helps you to focus your innate power to heal your back pain, it also brings your mind and body and existence together as one entity. This makes separating your back pain from you as a "person" futile. Mindful breathing powerfully focuses your mind on your back, and guides you through breathing relief into it in a structured and easy way, which you can do anywhere, anytime.

First take a breath in through your nose with your mouth closed. If you can't do this for any reason, then breathe through your mouth. It'll work just as well. Hold it for the count of four in your mind and then exhale. Make the breaths in and the breaths out the same in length. Breathe in to the count of five. Hold your breath for the count of four. Now breathe out to the count of five. Good. Now we have a breathing pattern established.

Now this time, when you breathe in, I want you to breathe in so that your stomach rises, to the count of five. Hold it for the count of four and then exhale to the count of five. Do this three times.

Now we come to the part where this exercise works so well with the relief of pain. This time, as you breathe in, in the same way you breathed into your stomach, I want you to imagine breathing into the pain in your back to the count of five, as though you are literally filling that whole area with oxygen. Then hold it for the count of four and exhale to the count of five. As you do this again, imagine that, as you fill the area in your back with oxygen, when you breathe out you begin to breathe out the pain that was there. Imagine each breath out takes more and more of the pain away. This is a great technique to practice daily, and I know a lot of my clients really enjoy it as its taking control in a powerful way through the natural process of breathing. Embrace your back pain, empower your very existence in this world as a unique human being, and experience the ultimate relief through the power of you.

Time to Rate It!

So, now you've practiced mindfulness, it's time to see how this has impacted your intensity level from Chapter 1. Become aware of your back now and rate it.

"Presently my intensity rating of pain is _____."

Keep practicing being mindful and begin to explore other ways of getting yourself into this powerful state for change, as this will help with what you will learn in the following chapters.

Bonus Gift Number 2!

I wanted you to get really accustomed to being mindful in this chapter, but now I am going to give you your second Bonus Gift to make becoming mindful even easier – My "Eliminate Stress Hypnotically" MP3 download is one of my most popular recordings and I'm giving it to you now. Simply go to www.TomBarberMedia.com and you will be able to download your copy absolutely free!

Chapter 3
Step 2: Your Ultimate Outcome
A Pain Free Life

What Do You *Really* Want in Being Pain Free?

I remember many years ago visiting my grandmother. She had suffered for a long time from arthritis, and her hands were painfully clenched in a claw-like position. She was a prolific knitter, and I recall with equal fondness and despair the intricate jumpers she knitted me and my two brothers, which of course had to be worn! Our jumpers were not of an inferior quality, don't get me wrong; they were sometimes, however, not the design that a young lad wanted to be seen in with his friends. Anyway, my grandmother knitted furiously, and this led to her hands becoming clenched with arthritis in the most painful way. It wasn't just her hands though; she also had arthritis in her feet, ankles, elbows and most of her joints. This meant that in her later years she was unable to carry things around as she had once done, and relied on help from her family.

I turned up at my grandmother's house one sunny day and knocked on her door. No answer. I knocked again. Again there was no answer. So I went to her window, which looked through to her living room, and there she was dancing around to Julio Iglesias, who, for those that are not of that era, was an old time Spanish crooner. So, there was my grandmother wracked with arthritis, dancing around the living room, and I simply looked on agape. How could she be in so much pain, yet move so well? I was getting no answer from the door, so I knocked on the window, and watched as, in one fell swoop, she buckled over and the pain swamped her face! So, was she putting it on? Absolutely not! She had simply been brought back to her reality.

So many people want to be rid of their pain, but have often thought no further than the pain they are experiencing, and what this will be like in the future. It's like they get locked into it. On the odd occasion something else comes along and distracts them completely, they just let loose, feel free and enjoy living, as though the pain wasn't even there. On that day, Julio Iglesias was my grandmother's distraction. People suffering from back pain experience this in their own unique way on many occasions. A moment of freedom that is sadly too short.

So, what to do about this? Do we simply wait for these moments to occur, or do we plan life with less pain and how it can be? What's stopping us from being pain free? How will life be with less pain? Will we lose something when it's gone? Are there any gains in not having it?

I may sound like I've lost the plot in saying that you are *gaining* something from your back pain, but it's not that simple. We are talking here about an out-of-awareness subconscious gain, not what you've planned or are consciously aware of. You sure aren't making it up, but there could be some inner unconscious reasons why your back pain persists. So, let's explore this train of thought further.

The Well-formed Outcome is a strategy for unpacking behaviours that is most well known from the behavioural communication model of neuro-linguistic programing - or NLP for short. Extensively written about by Bodenhammer and Hall (2001) in *The User's Manual for the Brain*, it offers us an advanced way of breaking down the nuances of our behaviour so that we can see where we want to go, what might be stopping us and what can help us. The whole point of NLP is about getting specific, direct and clear as to what we want, so we know what it is we are creating. The WFO helps us do just this.

So, take a pen and paper now, or use the spaces below to record your answers, and let's get specific! Take each question one at a time. There are no right or wrong answers. Let your mind run free and see what comes. The only rule is that you need to answer each question in turn. Do not move on to the next one until you are fully satisfied you have written what you need to say for each question.

Read the questions and complete the sentences one by one.

The 15-Step WFO

1. What do you want from becoming free of back pain?

I want ...

2. What does being pain-free do for you?

Being free of back pain ...

3. How will you know when you are free of back pain? For example, what do you picture yourself doing?

Imagine that in three different situations.
   a. At work I …

   b. Socially I …

   c. In my relationship I …

4. Imagine that has all happened. What do your thoughts tell you?

Imagine that in three different situations.
   a. At work I'm thinking …

   b. Socially I'm thinking …

   c. In my relationship I'm thinking …

5. Imagine that all this has actually happened. How do you feel about these images?
I am totally free of back pain and I feel …

6. Do you need help to maintain this way of being, or can you do it on your own?

   a. I need …

   b. I can …

7. When you are free of back pain, what do you most notice? Think of:

Step 2: Your Ultimate Outcome

    a.   Where I experience being free of back pain
The place I most notice being free of back pain is …

    b.   When I experience being free of back pain
The time I most notice being free of back pain is …

    c.   With whom I experience being free of back pain
The person or people I'm with when I most notice being free of back pain is …

    8.   When do you definitely NOT want back pain?
I NEVER want back pain when …

    9.   When you're totally free of back pain, is there anything negative about that which could have a detrimental impact on your life?
Being free of back pain might be difficult because …

    10. What would you need to make you pain free?
To be pain free I need …

    11. What could stop you achieving the ultimate relief from back pain?
The only thing that could stop me from being free from this back pain is …

    12. When you are free of back pain, what positive benefits of *having it* might you lose?
Because I am now free of back pain I may lose …

    13. Is becoming free of back pain worth the cost in money?
Yes / No

14. Is becoming free of back pain worth the cost in time?

Yes / No

15. Does being free of back pain agree with your sense of self; that is, who you believe you are?

Yes / No

So, how was it? These can seem like simple questions, but when asked in this way they powerfully unpack the whole experience of your back pain, your expectations, wishes and potential blocks. Only once you have "been unearthed", and acknowledged your blocks, can you rid yourself of them. When you can fully imagine this pain free possibility then you will naturally alter your present thoughts, feelings and behaviours in line with this. When you've reached this stage, only then can you really congruently look at the you of the future, the you that is living life with the ultimate relief.

Let's now take your Well-formed Outcome and bring it alive!

The Amazing Miracle Scenario!

Imagine that after reading this book something amazing happens. Actually … imagine this now: that you put this book down … right now, and that the pain in your back has completely disappeared, like it never was. It never happened. Perhaps you need to fast forward a bit. You've read this paragraph, and then tonight you go to sleep, wake up, and in the morning notice that during your sleep, something incredible has occurred. Your back pain has completely and totally disappeared. Completely gone, like it never happened, ever!

Step 2: Your Ultimate Outcome

Answer the following questions, and record your responses below:

1. What is the first thing you notice that tells you your back pain has permanently gone, forever?

2. What are you able to do now, that you couldn't do before, that tells you definitively that your back pain has completely gone?

3. Imagine the rest of your day, as you go through your day, totally free of back pain. What happens as you get out of bed, have breakfast, go to work, take lunch, finish work, travel home, eat your evening meal and eventually go to bed?

4. Begin to be aware of not only your reaction to these situations, but also to who else notices that you are totally free of back pain. Imagine people seeing you pain free. What tells them that this amazing change has happened?

Until you have some tangible idea of what it will be like to live without the pain in your back, you'll struggle to get anywhere. It is often the most difficult part of therapy. When you picked up this book, did you really expect to be free of your back pain, or did you see this as just another "maybe?" Maybe this book will help? Maybe, after all the other ways I've tried, this will be the one? Just maybe, I'll get some relief?

The questions above all come from a belief that you will never be free of the pain in your back. It's a maybe, a possible, a perhaps, but what you really need is to know *exactly* how it will be when your back pain has gone. No maybe, possibly, or perhaps, but a real sense of what, how, and when you will have the ultimate relief and how it will be. My clients and groups are often left bemused by these questions at first, as many of them have never even considered a future without back pain. So many of them are part of back pain support groups, spending a vast amount of their time with people that are talking about pain, and engaged in how *bad* it is. Think about it … do you really want to *support* your back pain?

Let's explore each question in more depth, one at a time:

1. *What is the first thing you notice that tells you your back pain has permanently gone, forever?*

You wake up, and bang! The first thing you notice as you jump out of bed is that you are able to move freely … to bend, stretch, grab and reach. What is the first thing that really springs out to you?

2. *What are you able to do now, that you couldn't do before, that tells you definitively that your back pain has completely gone?*

As we move on to this question, we begin to look at how this change affects the wider areas of your life. Without your back pain, what are you able to do that you couldn't do before … and in what different situations does this change affect you?

Step 2: Your Ultimate Outcome

I worked with a client once who, the morning after one of our sessions, was making lunch for one of her young children in the kitchen. The child in question was sitting up at the breakfast table with her other two siblings. As young children do, an argument broke out and her child ended up falling off her chair. My client rushed over and swooped down to pick her daughter up off the floor. As she stood straight and placed her daughter back in the chair, she suddenly realised what she had done. She hadn't moved like that for years! She bent down to the floor, and then stood straight. It seemed to her miraculous, yet this was one of the things she had spoken about missing dearly … her inability to be with her children in the way she thought she should. In simply exploring this question she unlocked what she passionately wanted back in her life, and this alone was a motivator for a change in her behaviour.

There is a point where we suddenly become incredibly clear that things are not what they once were. What is this point for you? What is the definitive moment that tells you that this ultimate relief is real?

3. *Imagine the rest of your day, totally free of back pain. What happens as you get out of bed, have breakfast, go to work, take lunch, finish work, travel home, eat your evening meal and eventually go to bed?*

This next step begins to make your awareness real. It brings the change that's happened to typical, everyday situations. It begins a new "movie" playing in your mind; a different you, not defined by your back pain. We begin to see how what was normal before, like how you got out of bed, got dressed, prepared and had breakfast, began your working day, and managed that day was, through the differences that now have happened. When we experience pain, it is very often felt from moment to moment. We can lose the continuity of our experiencing of life, and the pain just all rolls into one long sense of suffering and managing.

4. *Begin to be aware of not only your reaction to these situations, but also to who else notices that you are totally free of back pain. Imagine people looking at you pain free. What tells them that this amazing change has happened?*

Now we move out of your own experience of your back pain and into others' experience of you as a person free of back pain. This can be a powerful insight. Suffering from pain can affect the way you look. The strain can be seen on your face and you can get isolated into the pain experience, yet when we look at you without back pain from another's perspective, then we can see something else. When you ask the question, "How have I looked to others with my back pain?" and then "How do I look now, without it?" and see the difference and enjoy the feeling, you are then a step closer to actually living in a pain-free world.

So, ask yourself, who notices you moving differently? What do they see you doing? How might it be for them to see you like this? Asking these questions really takes you out of yourself and gets you to think of you as a person without back pain, and see who you are without it. Do you describe yourself as a back pain sufferer? Not anymore!

Being Incredibly Clear on What a Pain-Free-You Means! – Time to TOTE It!

So, you now have an image of the you that you want to be, a you that does not live life with the label of back pain sufferer. It's time to make this real at a deeper level, time to test how it fits you. *It's time to TOTE it!*

The TOTE process was first written about by Miller, Galanter and Pribram (1960) in *Plans and the Structure of Behaviour*. It has also been used effectively in neuro-linguistic programming by Robert Dilts in his work on aligning logical levels. Whenever we create a change in our behaviour or reaction to a particular situation there is a need to test that the new desired behaviour or reaction really fits us. The TOTE process helps us do just this.

TOTE stands for *Test - Operate - Test - Exit*. A simple example of the TOTE process can be found in the common experience of driving a car. When we make a journey, we usually have the route planned out before we begin. At certain points of the journey we know we will have to make specific turnings to reach our destination, and so for each part of the journey we use the TOTE process as follows:

- *Test* - Is this the correct turnoff? – No.
- *Operate* - Keep driving.
- *Test* - Is this the correct turnoff? – Yes.
- *Exit.*

The very same process is used for baking a cake.

- *Test* - Is the cake baked yet? – No.
- *Operate* - Close the oven door and bake for more time.
- *Test* - Is the caked baked now? – Yes.
- *Exit* - Remove the cake from the oven.

The process basically involves us using this strategy to see if what we are doing is leading us to our desired goal. While reading each chapter of this book, you are already using the TOTE process. You *Test* the technique you are learning, and if it doesn't get you the relief you're looking for, then you *Operate* by practicing some more, or reading the next chapter, and you *Test* again to see if your back pain is better, and if not you *Operate* again by practicing further, or reading the next chapter, and then you *Test* again and *Operate* again and *Test* again until you have the relief you want and then you *Exit* by stopping reading.

Remember the TOTE as you read through this book. In this chapter, if you are not clear as to your well-formed outcome then you will need to *Operate* a little more by going back to the WFO questions and fine tuning your responses. Keep doing this until it fits and you feel clear with where you are heading, and only then *Exit* to the next chapter. Happy TOTEing!

Time to Rate It!

"Presently my intensity rating of pain is _____."

Bonus Gift Number 3!

There is so much about the power of your imagination that you can learn about, and so I'm going to send you to get your next Bonus Gift now - Your 10-Part Email Course in Hypnosis and NLP! Simply go to www.TomBarberMedia.com, order your course, and begin your journey now!

Chapter 4
Step 3: Deconstructing Your Experience of Pain

Pain Metaphorically – Welcome to the Story of Your Pain

At the beginning of this book I told you a story about one of my own experiences of pain. There was a reason for this. Stories are a powerful way of conveying your message to another person. We tend to respond to change the most when we can resonate and connect with what we are hearing or reading, and there is an underlying message in it. This is why fairy tales convey such powerful messages to children. Tell children "Don't ..." And they do! Tell them a story of why they shouldn't, and the message tends to be heard.

Getting Creative in the Workshop

There are countless theories about how the mind works and how we operate as human beings. I want to keep matters simple here. Why? ... Because getting bogged down in numerous theories of the mind is not helpful in getting relief from your back pain. It's very likely that you've searched for endless ways to gain relief, and read countless theories as to why you have the pain in your back. The wonderful accessibility of information through the Internet means you have a vast store of information about back pain at your fingertips, but how much of it has actually helped? Some of it, possibly, some of it not at all. It's important, however, to have a place to start from.

The Mind Inc.

So, let's look at the mind in a simple metaphorical way. Imagine your mind is a company. In every company there is a hierarchy. There is a top management structure, a middle management, and then the workforce. Companies run this way because there needs to be a leaders' vision that is relayed and organised through a middle management, with tasks and goals being carried out. That way the organisation runs efficiently and delivers what it should.

If we look at the mind in this way, we can break it down into a similar three-tier structure.

1. The conscious mind – The top management.
2. The intermediate subconscious mind – The middle management.
3. The base subconscious mind – The workforce.

The conscious "managing director"

This part of the mind can be seen as being responsible for the same kind of roles a managing director would be involved in. It is the intelligent part of the mind that has the ability to learn, understand and make judgements based on reason. It can analyse situations and then make management decisions based on the information coming from middle management.

Imagine you are flying away on holiday somewhere far away for the next two weeks. Last year, when you packed your suitcase, you made sure you had everything you needed for your holiday, and after sitting on your suitcase, so you could do the zips up, struggled carrying it to the airport. When you reached the check in desk and your luggage was weighed it was 20Ibs overweight, costing you a small fortune in additional charges. Still, considering that you needed *everything* packed into your case, you paid the charges and continued your journey, only to find that at the end of your holiday you had worn less than half the clothes you'd packed! So ... this year you make a mental note, a few weeks before you begin packing, that for your holiday to be more cost effective, you'll only pack half the clothes you did last year. You note also that you won't strain yourself the way you did last year, in trying to carry a case you could hardly lift. Your conscious managing director has done its job.

The intermediate "middle management" subconscious mind

This part of the mind relies on memory and a skilful kind of cleverness that informs the decisions and judgements of the conscious mind, and also implements them as procedures with labels and processes. It fulfils the role of middle management, or the warehouse manager, and puts the decisions made at the top into action. It also has the role of managing, organising and motivating the workforce.

So, back to your holiday preparations. The conscious managing director has passed down the decision that this year your suitcase needs only half the amount of clothes that were packed last year, and needs to be of a weight that fits the airline baggage allowance limit. So you begin to consider, from what wasn't worn on holiday last year, which clothes to pack this time, and how much that which gets packed into your case weighs. You plan a procedure for "packing" that adheres to the directions of the conscious managing director, and which fits your calculations.

The base subconscious "workforce" mind

This is the part of the mind that it all comes down to - the workforce. As important as the conscious and intermediate subconscious are, unless there are "workers" in place to implement the practical production tasks, then the company will fail. This is where the mind and this analogy of a company bear so much similarity. The base subconscious is the part of the mind that takes care of your bodily functions. It is the workshop, the repair centre, the signalling centre and, just like any workforce, it also influences the running of the system. This then is the part of the mind we need to be working with when we're looking at the changes we want to actually happen. It has the most influence in the system. If the "management" disappear for the day on a long lunch break, the company or organisation will continue working and producing. But ... if the workers walk out, nothing will get done!

The best way to motivate workers within a company is through stories of others' successes, and selling a sense of pride and quality in one's work. That's why companies set goals and targets, and offers bonuses if the work gets completed in the time scale given, and to the satisfaction of the management. The mind works in the same way.

One of the best ways to reach the base subconscious mind is through visualising the change slowly taking place. Rarely do changes anywhere happen overnight. They take a gradual change that then crawls and seeps into action. This is why the conscious managing director doesn't decide, on the day of your holiday, to hurriedly send a memo to the intermediate subconscious mind, expecting the required changes to be implemented immediately. The intelligent conscious mind knows that this takes time, and that there is a process to be applied by the warehouse manager. With these instructions in place the base workforce subconscious mind can collect the required clothes for your suitcase, and pack them, ready for your holiday. That is what the following technique is; the process your base subconscious mind needs to follow to get the job done. Once you implement it, the powerful force of your deep inner subconscious mind can get to work, doing what it needs to do.

So now, we are going to make a series of gradual changes in the way you hold your current experience of your back pain, to impact that influential base subconscious workshop of your mind, resulting in the changes you want taking place efficiently, effectively and effortlessly.

Pain: It's Like an Object

Imagine for a moment that you can actually look right down inside your back. Let's put this into context. I often remind my clients about a 1987 film called *Innerspace*, with Dennis Quaid, where an astronaut was shrunk in a laboratory miniaturization experiment and unwittingly placed inside a minute vessel that was then inserted into the bloodstream of a hypochondriacal person, who had only a limited amount of oxygen to survive.

The wonderful thing about our imagination is that whether you've seen this film or not, you've likely just imagined that process of a miniaturized you floating around in your body. So, travelling down inside your body now, make the journey to the area where you've felt all of that discomfort in your back. Do it now - go down in your mind to the part of your back that you feel the discomfort. When you are there, imagine that you put aside all the descriptions of the pain that you've ever expressed, and imagine the pain instead as *an object*.

What kind of object would it be? It could be a ball of pain, a cube, a tornado or a knife. However you imagine it, the main thing is that it needs to be from within your imagination. There's no need to take into account any medical understanding of the pain, as that isn't how the inner base subconscious mind works, and so isn't at all helpful. What we need is for you to put aside all logical and rational visions of the pain and simply let your subconscious mind find what the *symbolic* pain looks like for you, or how it is represented to you.

Let's start with this object's shape. What kind of shape is it? Is it circular? A square? Rectangular? A wave-like shape? Oblong or triangular? However you imagine the shape, let's begin now to work at changing its dimensions. Let's begin to change the symbolic image of the pain. However you imagine the shape of your pain, I want you now to imagine it slowly changing to a different shape.

Step 3: Deconstructing Your Experience of Pain

If it's round, begin to see corners emerge as it turns into a square.

If it's triangular, see the edges moving so the shape becomes a rectangle.

If it's square, make it a ball.

Whatever the shape is, slowly mould it into a different shape.

Next become aware of the *colour* of the new shape. Remember, this shape is the symbolic image of the pain in your back. What colour is it? Is it a bright or dull colour? Is it a pastel type of colour or luminous? Whatever the colour is, just try to get as distinct an image of the colour as you can.

The next step now is to change the colour to an entirely different one. Make it as different a colour as you can, on the other end of the colour spectrum, so if it's black, make it white, or if it's red, turn it into a green image.

Next, imagine the size of the shape: the size of your back pain. Is it big or small? Maybe you can position the size of the object of the pain next to something, another image, so you can get a sense of the size of it. Imagine that the larger the shape, the more intense the pain is, and the smaller the shape the less intense the pain. So now begin to change the size of the shape.

Remember, your imagination is infinitely creative, so you could simply shrink the object, or you could imagine sucking its energy away so it shrinks that way. You could compress the shape. Imagine what kind of tool would help you do that. If you imagine, for example, the pain shape as a balloon, how about popping the balloon with a needle so it shrinks right down? Your imagination is so powerful; you can creatively do whatever you need to do.

The key here is to keep playing around in your creative imagination with how you experience the object, as this is your inner symbolic representation of your back pain. Change its colour, shape, size and … keep changing it! As you practice doing this, you are changing the inner associations with how you have stored your back pain in your mind, and this will get your workforce reacting and doing something different!

I remember a long time ago, when I was in the armed forces, standing on a parade ground for hours on end, practicing and rehearsing marching up and down in a line. I didn't much realise the point of the exercise at the time, but it was a massive form of suggestion to simply follow orders. Through this repetition, however, I developed a powerful unconscious learning, where my body *automatically* responded in a specifically trained way, upon hearing a particular command. Knowing what I know now, I can see how highly effective it was. Practising and rehearsing over and over again, is a powerful method of re-writing how you respond to a situation.

I remember one drill exercise in particular, where my colleagues and I were standing and waiting to be inspected by the officer in charge. We were standing still on one single spot for around two hours, in the searing heat of the sun, before the colonel came to inspect my section of the parade ground. I remember one of my colleagues fainting, horrifyingly falling on his bayonet, and then being carried away to the medic's office to be patched up. I recall clearly the pain I felt in my heels, like a red hot poker kind of sensation as if scalding hot skewers were being pushed into my heels from the ground upwards. It felt so painful that my mind just kept focussing on the pain, and this is where I learnt, very rapidly, to use my imagination to change what I was experiencing. The last thing I wanted was to fall on the twelve-inch blade hovering precariously around my armpit. I changed in my mind the pain sensation and imagined it becoming wider, and then changed its colour and then changed its size, and then got creative in my mind and imagined the sensation was like a river of cool water flowing up through my body. I know this was the only way I got through that inspection, and it worked like magic!

As you change your own back pain sensation, note where your creative imagination takes you. Keep practicing and get proficient at changing what your mind perceives. Remember, the most powerful influence comes from your base subconscious, deep within. It's the workshop, the worker, the salesperson, the accountant, and so many other roles within you. Look after it, and it will look after you.

Time to Rate It!

Again, now it's time to see what this chapter has done for your intensity rating.

"Presently my intensity rating of pain is _____."

Keep playing around in your imagination with the different feelings you experience in your back. Make the sensation into an object, and away you go!

Chapter 5
Step 4: Reframe for the Ultimate Gain

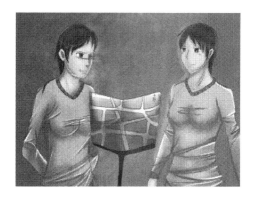

The AVADKOG Experience - What's that?

Neuro-linguistic programming is a method of getting deeper understanding as to how we communicate, not only with others, but with ourselves. The NLP communication model has been around since the 1970's but has crept more and more into areas of everyday life over the last few years. NLP is now used not only as a way for salespeople to increase their rapport with potential customers, but is also used in education, business, coaching, nursing and the health industry as communication skills become an ever more important part of our culture.

The NLP model is vast in its uses and helps us understand not just how we communicate, but how we process information, and this is where it comes in incredibly helpful in the treatment of pain. When you think about your back pain, how do you experience it? Do you focus solely on the feeling of it, the tactile sensory experience?

Do you experience it more in your thoughts, a conversation with yourself about it in your head? Or do you experience the "sound" of your pain, the shooting, searing, throbbing resonating throughout you in an auditory way? Maybe you just see the pain in your mind, even imagining the "instrument" that could be causing it? Is it a needle or hot iron searing through your back, or is your back on fire?

Whilst we may think that everybody experiences pain internally in the same way, this isn't the case. Have you ever tried to explain your back pain to somebody and you feel they just don't seem to understand, whilst another person gets it completely? Here we see how one person's sensory experience of pain can work very differently from another's. If you can gain greater understanding of how *you* experience pain, then you have a better chance of influencing that experience.

NLP offers an excellent way of unearthing how your sensory experience of pain works, through what it calls AVADKOG – or *Auditory-Visual-Auditory Digital-Kinaesthetic-Olfactory-Gustatory*. What does all this mean to you and pain, though? All of these sensory modalities explain the various ways you experience the outer world, and how you make sense of those experiences within you. This is done through what you hear (Auditory), see (Visual), your inner dialogue (Auditory Digital), your bodily sensations and feelings (Kinaesthetic), smell (Olfactory), and taste (Gustatory). The relevance of this lies in knowing how we "code" our experience of pain in this *sensory* way. It's likely that *one* of these sensory experiences, these modalities, will be favoured within you as a way of organising your world, but we experience that world through all of our senses, to a greater or lesser degree. Through exploration, we can find out *how* those sensory experiences work within you, enabling them to be altered, thus changing your pain experience.

So, what's your favoured sensory modality? Well, let's look at some common experiences that may unlock how you experience your personal world. Have you ever purchased a car, some clothing, or a piece of furniture? When you did, you used a complex system of choice to purchase that item.

Let's take a car. What's important for you about a car? How it looks, the colour, or how sleek its curves are? Or maybe you love to get in the car and rev up the engine to hear how the car sounds, how quickly the engine revs up and down, and what sort of "clunk" the door makes when it closes. What may be more important for you is how the car feels, so the comfort of the driver's seat, the feel of the steering wheel, the texture of the seats, and the engine vibrations you get from the accelerator pedal. What might be more at the top of your list of priorities are the technical specifications of the car, how far it goes on a full tank of fuel, and what mechanical history it has, because all that's important to you is buying a car from a logical and sensible place. Of course all of these might hold some importance, but one of them will be the game changer, or what really makes you ultimately feel comfortable enough to buy that car, what sells it to you enough to make the purchase. If you are the sort of person then that organises the world primarily from your *visual* sensory modality, then it's likely to be what you see about the car, how it looks to you that brings you to the game-changer point. If you are more an *auditory* sensory organiser, then how the car sounds will be key, and if you process more from a *kinaesthetic* sensory place, then the feel of the car is what's important to you. Think about one of your recent purchasing experiences and your buying patterns. Where do you think you fit?

Let's now relate this to your experience of pain. If you imagine your back pain as "fire", do you *see* the flames raging away, do you *hear* the crackling of the fire or do you *feel* the searing heat? It's these three sensory modalities that we are going to focus on in this chapter: how you experience what you see, hear and feel in your encounter of pain in order to change your experience of back pain to one of relief.

Mapping Across - Brain Change Process Step 1 – The Pain

We've explored above the general sensory modalities of visual, auditory and kinaesthetic. The finer points, the nuances, or details of what we see, such as the colours, or of what we hear, such as the volume or tone, and what we feel, as in the texture or temperature, are what we call the *submodalities* - these are the qualities of the three sensory modalities. It's through making a change in these submodalities in your mind that we can alter how you experience pain through reprogramming, or recoding it.

So let's get started with Step 1. Firstly, begin to become aware of the sensory experience of your back pain. If you're not feeling the pain at the moment, then imagine you are back in the last time you experienced it. When you are there, and back in it, then complete the Submodalities Choice Indicator Scale 1 below – and do it as quickly as you can. The faster you do it, the closer to the sensory experience you'll get, so don't think about it too much; just go for it and circle the descriptions that most suit your experience of the pain.

Figure 5:1 Submodalities Choice Indicator Scale 1 – The Pain

Visual	Auditory	Kinaesthetic
When you imagine the pain, is it …	*When you imagine the pain, does it sound …*	*When you imagine the pain, you experience it as …*
Black & White OR Colour	Loud OR Quiet	Large OR Small in Size
Bright OR Dim	Fast Paced OR Slow Paced	High OR Low in Intensity
Two Dimensional OR Three Dimensional	High Tone OR Low Tone	Hot OR Cool
A Moving Picture OR Still Image	High Pitch OR Low Pitch	Heavy OR Light
A Small OR Large Picture	Like It's Coming from the Inside OR Outside	Hard OR Soft
With a Frame OR No Frame	Like It's Coming from the Left OR Right	Abrasive OR Smooth
In Focus OR Out of Focus	Intermittent OR Continuous	Its Location is in my …

Mapping Across - Brain Change Process Step 2 – The Ultimate Relief

Now for Step 2. Take a few moments to clear your mind. Think of somewhere that you are really able to relax completely. Calm your mind and relax. And now, begin to let your mind drift to a time before you *ever* experienced the pain. Remember what it was like, the era of your life, your age, where your imagination takes you, and really let yourself sink into the feeling of relief. When you're there, complete the second Submodalities Choice Indicator Scale 2 below – and again, do it as quickly as you can. Remember, the faster you do it the closer to the sensory experience you'll get, so don't think about it too much. Just go for it and circle the descriptions that this time most suit your experience of the pain.

Figure 5:2 Submodalities Choice Indicator Scale 2 – The Ultimate Relief

Visual	Auditory	Kinaesthetic
When you imagine the pain, is it …	*When you imagine the pain, does it sound …*	*When you imagine the pain, you experience it as …*
Black & White OR Colour	Loud OR Quiet	Large OR Small in Size
Bright OR Dim	Fast Paced OR Slow Paced	High OR Low in Intensity
Two Dimensional OR Three Dimensional	High Tone OR Low Tone	Hot OR Cool
A Moving Picture OR Still Image	High Pitch OR Low Pitch	Heavy OR Light
A Small OR Large Picture	Like It's Coming from the Inside OR Outside	Hard OR Soft
With a Frame OR No Frame	Like It's Coming from the Left OR Right	Abrasive OR Smooth

Step 4: Reframe for the Ultimate Gain

In Focus OR Out of Focus	Intermittent OR Continuous	Its Location is in my ...

Mapping Across - Brain Change Process Step 3 – Define the Differences

Now you have done this it's time to create the powerful change you want to gain you the ultimate relief. Now we are ready for step 3.

Step 3. Compare the coding of pain in Submodalities Indicator Scale 1, and the coding of relief in Scale 2. What's important to make a distinct note of here is what visual, auditory and kinaesthetic *differences* there are. Many of your choices may be the same, but we are only interested in what differences there are. There may be only two or three, but that's all we need.

So, if in image 1 your visual image of the pain area was black and white, and in image 2 (the relief picture) it was still black and white, then we are not interested in that. However, if in image 1 it was black and white and in image 2 it was colour, then we will call that a difference. Similarly, if the sound associated with the pain in image 1 was loud, and it was loud in relief image 2, then again we don't count that. If it was, however, loud in image 1 but quiet in image 2, then we will mark that as a difference. And if the feeling was hot in image 1 and 2 then we don't count that either, but if it was hot in 1 and cool in 2, then we also mark that as a difference.

Mapping Across - Brain Change Process Step 3 – Overlaying

See it ... Hear it ... Feel it ... Differently!

57

Now, you should have a clear distinction between the sensory submodalities you got from image 1 and those in image 2, and be able to see what stayed the same and what was different. It's the differences that will make the change you want, so now we can put to use the creative work with changing the pain, as you did with it as an object in the previous chapter.

So, for step 3, begin to become aware again of your back pain, and especially your sensory experience of it. If it's not there at the moment, then once again imagine you are back in the last time you experienced it.

Imagine the experience of your back pain, and begin to make it real. Bring it alive, focusing on the submodalities experience, what you *see*, *hear* and *feel* in relation to the pain. This time, however, we are going to make the required changes. This time when you imagine your sensory experience of pain via the image 1 description, change the image 1 experience at the points where you identified the sensory *differences* in the step 2 descriptions. Imagine each visual, auditory and kinaesthetic part of the back pain experience, and then make the vital changes identified with the differences in place.

So, as you imagine the image 1 pain experience and the visual part was bright, but dim in image 2, then make your imaginary pain experience dim. If the sound was coming in image 1 from the inside, and from the outside in image 2, then change that in your imaginary visualisation. Similarly, if the feeling from image 1 was hot, and cool from image 2, then your visualisation should make that change, from hot to cool. Remember, everything else stays the same. Just make the shift between the differences only.

Step 4: Reframe for the Ultimate Gain

Take yourself through this visualisation now five times with the different changes in place. Soon you'll begin to find that the image you'll begin to carry around in your mind is of you living without back pain, as you will have the sensory associations *now* to no back pain. You have given your workforce, your base subconscious mind, a whole new set of instructions to follow.

Ready for Another Step Further? - Think it ... Taste it ... and Smell the Change!

Changing the mental image you used to carry around of you living with back pain, through changing your stored sensory coding, is a powerful method for changing your inner perceptions, to you now living in a pain free reality. Our senses don't just stop at what we see, hear and feel as we've explored above, however. So, to fine tune this change even further, we're now going to add another adjustment.

Remember AVADKOG from earlier? Well, we've focused on the three modalities of Auditory, Visual and Kinaesthetic, and now we can do our further fine tuning by changing the Auditory Digital (your self-speak), Olfactory (smell) and Gustatory (taste) parts of your experiencing of your back pain. For that we are going to add a simple reframe, which means we need to look at what would be more useful for you to experience with these senses.

Reframing

Begin with your current internal self-speak. In the two blank spaces below, write your current self-speak statement about your back pain, so maybe your current thought reads something like: "This damn back pain gets me down." Then think of an alternative preferred thought that you'd like to have instead, such as: "My back is speaking to me, what is it saying?" This sense of curiosity leads to a useful distraction away from the pain - to the *purpose* of the pain. Or, your current thought might be, "My back always hurts, and stops me from doing anything," and your preferred thought could be, "My back is uncomfortable when I get up in the morning, but it eases, and I'm able to do what I need to, as the day goes on."

Think about your own thoughts now in relation to your back pain, and when you have a definite statement record it below. Then, think about your preferred thought, and record that below also.

Current Thought:

Preferred Thought:

Now do the same for the "smell" of your back pain. Imagine the pain has a smell. It might be a smell that disgusts you. Rotten fish or eggs are common ones. Then imagine a smell that you like. Complete the sentences below.

Current Smell: My back pain smells like …

Preferred Smell: Now, my back pain smells like …

Now do the same for the "taste" of your back pain. Think of a taste that you hate, and change it to one that you love. Again, record it below.

Step 4: Reframe for the Ultimate Gain

Current Taste: My back pain tastes like …

Preferred Taste: Now, my back pain tastes like …

Once again, imagine the thought, smell and taste as vividly as you can, and repeat each change in sensation a few times. Remember that the more you can mentally alter the perception of how you hold your back pain via your senses, the more you influence your inner experience of it.

Time to Rate It!

"Presently my intensity rating of pain is _____."

You are half way through the Ultimate Relief programme now, and will be getting an idea of what techniques are helping you the most. Keep practicing with all of them, and if you find that your creative mind presents you with something that works even better, when you practice the techniques, then go with it. It's about finding what works best for you. As Henry Ford, the founder of the Ford Motor Company said, "If you always do what you've always done, you'll always get what you've always got." Do what works, and if it isn't working, do something else, and if that doesn't work, do something else! This, remember, is the essence of TOTE. To quote Robert Allen, the motivational business author, "There is no failure, only feedback."

At this stage, I really want to know how you have got on with the techniques you have learned so far. Go now to www.TheBookOnBackPainFeedback.com and take a few minutes to update me on what's helped you and how you're using the book. Once you have submitted your feedback, you will then be able to access *The Book on Back*

Pain social media programme where you can find out how others are using and benefitting from what you are learning. You may get some great tips!

Chapter 6
Step 5: The Headquarters

The Master Control Room of Your Mind

In this chapter you will learn another metaphor that enables you to take charge of your pain, and turn it down. The intricate workings of the mind have often been linked to that of a computer, so let's use this analogy to teach the subconscious middle management how to reassert control of the over exuberant base subconscious workforce, which has slightly lost its way in regulating your pain.

Imagine you were able to simply switch your experience of pain off. Literally - imagine reaching out and flicking a switch and the pain is gone. The pain disappears and you experience a wonderful sense of no-feeling. Sound a little dramatic? Well - how about reaching out and moving a dial so that the intensity of your experience of pain is turned down from, say, 10 down to 5, or 4 or 1! Is that easier?

Wouldn't it be amazing if it were that simple? Well, I have used this method in my workshops and with clients with just this kind of amazingly powerful outcome. If everybody suffering from pain were able to simply imagine this visualisation, then wouldn't it make a difference? Probably not - because it requires not only conscious awareness for the visualisation to take effect, but a deeper subconscious *reaction* to the suggestions of change within the process, to get the change required - "Middle to Base subconscious … Do you copy?"

In this chapter we will begin to explore the state of hypnosis, which can enable this necessary deeper unconscious change to take place. First of all, remember how we rated your experience of pain in chapter 1. Again, you can use either the Wong-Baker (2001) FACES™ Pain Rating Scale:

Or the simple numerical scale below, to rate the intensity of the pain:

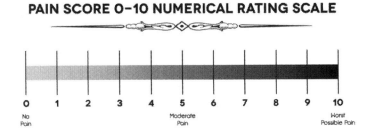

The main thing is that you have a way of gauging what changes and how much less you experience pain as we

Step 5: The Headquarters

move through the technique. This is what helps you capture the changes and make them real for you.

So, once you have chosen your intensity level at this stage, we can then move onto using the technique. First, however, you need to be able to take yourself into the hypnotic trance state that this technique really works well with.

Self-Hypnosis

There are many different ways you can use self-hypnosis, all of which are safe, effective and will help the visualisations you will be doing in this chapter to bring about the changes you want. If you haven't used self-hypnosis before, you're also about to learn a very simple yet extremely effective method for harnessing the incredible power of your subconscious mind to do great things for you. If you haven't already downloaded my "Eliminate Stress Hypnotically" Bonus MP3, then remember you can get your very own copy right now at www.TomBarberMedia.com and yes ... it's my FREE gift to you! Listening to my recording for just twenty minutes per day will train you to switch off, let go and effortlessly drift into the hypnotic trance state so you can really get in touch with the vast potential you have within your mind. If you haven't already, go and download it now, listen and enjoy.

As well as me taking you through the process of relaxing deeply into hypnosis via my MP3, here are a three ways you can use self-hypnosis to take you into the optimal state of mind for change to use the next ultimate relief technique, the Master Control Room.

The Thumbnail Gazing Method

This method is particularly useful if you are not so good at using your mind to switch off and find it helpful to have something specific to focus on. Now hold your thumb out in front of you and fix your gaze on your thumbnail as shown below.

Don't let your focus wander; just keep focussing on your thumbnail. Then very slowly begin to bring your hand closer to your face, as if your thumbnail were making a direct line towards your nose. Remember to do this very slowly, as what you'll notice is that as your hand gets closer to your nose, and you keep your focus on your thumbnail, your eyes will begin to slowly defocus. When eventually your thumbnail touches the tip of your nose, you'll be struggling to keep any focus at all, and at that point you can just let your arm drop down into your lap and allow your eyes to close.

That's it; you've taken yourself into a light state of hypnotic trance. Practice it a few times before you move on to the next method.

Step 5: The Headquarters

The Eye-Breathing Method

The eye-breathing method is a slightly faster method of taking yourself into the hypnotic trance state. It's designed to regulate your breathing, which is often helpful in times of stress or anxiety, often an unwanted relative of pain. It also creates the eye tiredness needed to lead you into eye closure, where you can then begin the visualisation method that we will explore soon.

To begin, sit comfortably and settle your breathing as much as possible. When you are ready to begin, take a deep breath in, and at the same time move your eyes upwards as far as they can go. Count for two seconds and then breathe out completely, and as you breathe out, move your eyes as far down as they can go. Now repeat this two more times, and on the third breath out, as your eyes move down, just let your eyes close.

Again, this takes you into an early stage of the hypnotic trance state, which is all that's required for effective visualisation.

Deepening the Trance State

Once you have tried these two methods, you can get comfortable practicing them a few times so that they feel natural, and then we can add another method which will take you deeper into the hypnotic trance experience. This will begin to connect you to the inner resources of your subconscious mind, at which point you will be ready to move onto getting relief with the Master Control Room technique.

Artfully Vague

Considered the father of modern day hypnotherapy, Dr Milton Erickson (1901 – 1980) was renowned for his creative use of language to help his patients overcome countless difficulties, including pain. He believed, as do many schools of thought, that the person that knows the best how to overcome a problem is the person *with* the problem. They just have to be able to access the inner unconscious knowledge that will unlock the answers they need. Erickson was a uniquely talented master at using language to facilitate this process. His use of stories, metaphors and language, in an indirect and purposely vague way, really got to the heart of his patients' inner resources in a very short period of time.

The "artfully vague" method is designed to help you relax deeper into the trance state needed for this same kind of powerful change to take place, by getting you to choose what is relaxing for you, as opposed to imagining a commonly used visualisation of walking down a set of stairs, each step taking you deeper into a relaxed state, or walking along a hot sunny beach with the water rolling over your toes, each step getting more and more relaxed. The reason this artfully vague method works so well is that often, the conventional imaginary scenes used within relaxation methods can do the exact opposite of what they intended. If you've ever fallen down a set of stairs before, or hate hot sunny beaches, you'll recognise that these scenes simply wouldn't work for you! So, getting you to choose what distinctively works for you makes the relaxation experience unique and personal, and hence infinitely more powerful.

Step 5: The Headquarters

So, once you have got comfortable using one of the self-hypnosis methods above, the next step is to imagine the following scene. You can do this easily with your eyes open. We do this when we daydream all the time. Imagine the scene unfolding as follows:

You're drifting to a different place now, somewhere perhaps far away. Wherever you find yourself drifting to in your mind, it's simply a place where you can imagine completely and utterly switching off and relaxing very deeply. It may be somewhere that you've visited before in the past, or it could be somewhere you're planning to go to, or somewhere you'd really like to be, anywhere in the world. It could even be a place in your imagination. The only thing that matters is that in your place you can just simply let go, switch off and relax completely.

Nobody wants anything from you there or expects anything from you, and the only thing there is for you to do is relax deeply and soundly. When you are in that place, wherever it may be, then you can begin to bring it alive and make it real, as if you've been magically transported right back into that memory, or that experience, as if you are actually there, and begin to notice what you see around you, what different sights appear to you ... and then notice what sounds you begin to hear, and where those sounds are coming from.

It may even just be the sound of silence. And then you begin to notice the thoughts that drift through your mind there, and also you get a sense of how you feel in that place, both in your body and mind. In this place you can feel as completely relaxed as you ever have anywhere before. It's a special place of calm, peace and tranquillity, your special place, and you can just stay there and experience it, and let yourself be ...

Now, in this state of mind, you're ready to move onto the Master Control Room. You've got your pain intensity measure from earlier and its time now to engage your powerful inner mind to turn it down! Let your imagination go with it, and enjoy the journey.

Re-imprinting Your Brain for the Ultimate Relief: The Master Control Room

Imagine from your special place of relaxation and calm that you are going on a journey, a journey to your inner control room - the Master Control Room of your mind where everything is taken care of. The control room is where all of your bodily functions, emotions, thoughts and everything that happens inside you is controlled from. Put yourself at the entrance of the control room, standing in front of a door. Become aware of what colour the door is, and what size it is, and then gently push the door open and walk on into the control room. This is the control room of your mind, and inside here you can control, adjust, turn up, turn down, regulate and fine tune anything you want to.

As you walk through the control room, take a look around and just get a sense for all of the control panels, each one taking care of a specific function within you, so you'll notice that there are lots of control panels! You might notice also the sounds they make, whirring away as they regulate how you are working, from the inside out. You can notice walking past the panel with a sign at the top that reads "blood pressure" and notice the lights flashing and the sounds coming from the panel, and you can keep walking, next noticing the panel called "appetite" and the lights and sounds coming from that. Then you keep walking and come across the panel taking care of your breathing, and then one controlling your sleeping patterns, and then very soon you notice the panel you're looking for - "pain."

You go to the pain control panel now, and notice what you see, and the sounds your hear it making. On the panel there are a number of switches and buttons and dials and lights, each one controlling the levels and intensity of pain you experience, which can be shown through the indicator screen on the control panel. This is one of the most important panels in the master control room, as the experience of pain is most often what keeps you from danger and lets you know something needs attending to in your body. But with what you know about your own experience of pain, we can now safely make the adjustments needed to lower those sensations, turn down your experience of those unwanted feelings, quieten the pain thoughts and bring peace to any part of your body you desire.

Look at the panel now and notice the indicator and the intensity level it is at now - between 0 to 10 - the number it's set at now indicating the level of pain in your back that you want to reduce. Now, reach out and turn down the dial controlling the intensity ... and slowly turn it down lower ... and lower, until it reaches the level of intensity that your inner subconscious mind knows *instinctively* is the exact right level for you, where you can feel relief and comfort from all of those unwanted feelings.

As you turn it down, hear the noises of the control panel slowly changing and quietening down, and very soon the indicator shows the intensity level at just the right level for you. Notice what number it's showing now. Maybe it's down to 4, or 3 or 2. You'll know deep inside what's right for you. Just be guided by your mind. And when it's there, just feel the relief and the peace. Then you can move your attention to one of the switches or buttons that will lock that indicator at the correct setting, keeping it there so that it permanently stays in that position, controlling all of those old feelings of pain at the level that suits you.

When the indicator is locked off, then you can step away from the control panel and breathe a sigh of relief, as now … *you* are in control, you now are the one that dictates how that control panel works, and from this moment forward you become in charge of any changes that you need to make there, or indeed in any of the other panels in your Master Control Room.

Now, you can walk back through the Control Room and back to the exit, walking through the door and closing it tight behind you, letting yourself then drift back to your special place of calm and peaceful relaxation, and after a few moments you take a deep breath, return to full mindful awareness, and stretch.

Precision Adjustments

So, how was the experience for you? For the many people that I work with both in private one-to-one sessions and also in my Ultimate Relief workshops, this process works pretty much instantly. This is because it powerfully focuses your subconscious resources to regulating the experience of pain symbolically, which it can easily understand outside of the interruptions of the conscious mind, the sometimes all too "knowing" CEO. This symbolic connection creates powerful psychological and physical changes in the neurological messages being sent and received to the specific area of your back we've worked on.

Step 5: The Headquarters

Many people ask for how long the relief will remain, and the only answer to that is to remember that this process puts you back in charge, so it's up to you. Periodically revisiting the Control Room is both necessary and useful, as it trains you to take control of how you manage the feelings and experience, creating powerful changes.

So what other changes could we make? How could we make precision adjustments as to how the control panels work? There are an infinite number of ways we could use our creative imagination to do this. Some of my clients, upon visiting the Control Room again, search out other specific control panels, such as the anxiety panel, and in doing this fine tune their subconscious attention as to the changes that need to be made. Often, sufferers of back pain, due to walking differently or sitting differently to compensate for the pain, find that they start to experience pain in different parts of their back, or their legs or shoulders, and so on revisiting the Master Control Room, locate further control panels that regulate all of these different areas - the lower back, middle back, upper back, shoulders, legs or whatever else is causing them discomfort - and then work on mentally moving the dials and switches in each of the relevant control panels to address all of these different areas. It really is about becoming the master of your Master Control Room, and getting used to and skilful at taking control of *your* subconscious mind.

Maintaining Your CEO (Mind) Position

Taking control means taking *action*. I'm guessing you are reading this book because what you have tried up to now to rid yourself of back pain hasn't worked, or hasn't worked in the way you'd liked it to have done. It's as good to know what doesn't work, as it is to know what does. That you're reading this book already says that you are on the road to taking control of your back pain, trying different ways to find relief so you can live life without the discomfort and the stress that back pain can bring.

From now on … you are the Chief Executive Officer of your mind. There's a lot going on in there that you rarely have to think about, like how your heart keeps beating, how your body regulates your breathing, how you swallow when you need to, how your blood clots when necessary, how you blink automatically, and so much more. Your body is constantly renewing itself, replacing and regenerating cells to maintain a proper and efficient functioning of your system, and this you need never think about. That's amazing isn't it! Once in a while however, you need to take charge, look at your system and make changes, and the Master Control Room technique helps you do just that.

You might on occasion (I hope from reading this book) have some inspirational and creative ideas, and now, through this method, you can pass them down into your inner mind to action and implement. I had a client once who decided that on entering his Master Control Room that his whole control room was actually outdated, old and in need of a complete overhaul! So in his session, we spent time stripping out all the control panels, rewiring, knocking out a wall here and there to make room for some updated machines, and completely refitted the control room out. Symbolically fantastic - physically life-changing!

Of course, it doesn't have to be that drastic. You might find that instead of turning the dial down and locking it off with a dead switch that you move a lever, push a sequence

Step 5: The Headquarters

of buttons, or clean out the air vents that are causing the control panel to overheat and work well below its optimum capacity. This is the beauty of our creative mind. If something isn't working, stop it, and do something different. That's what a good CEO does, and now that you have overhauled new state of the art systems in place, you can do an awesome job of running you effectively. You can make your back pain redundant! If you have the inclination, sack your back pain. You're the boss. You can do that!

Time to Rate It!

"Presently my intensity rating of pain is _____."

In the next chapter you will be using the state of hypnosis again, so keep practicing the different self-hypnosis methods, and use them daily. They really will make a difference to your quality of life.

Chapter 7
Step 6: Handing It Over to You
Turn Your Pain Off!

At this point in the book we come to one of the most powerful methods of pain control and relief I've ever used with clients over many years of pain control work. It's called the Glove Anaesthesia Method, and it has helped countless clients of mine across the world to take control of their pain, instantly. Not only does this method help gain instant relief, but it puts you in control of managing any returning pain, once and for all.

Imagine now you can put on a "glove" of anaesthesia. You actually pull the glove on your hand and your whole hand becomes anaesthetised, so there is no sensation in it at all. Imagine then that you can transfer that anaesthetised sensation to any part of your back that you want to. That's exactly what you are going to learn to do in this technique – The Glove Anaesthesia Method. It's an incredibly potent way of using the power of your mind to create changes in your body. The underpinning of this technique rests on two powerful methods of influencing both feelings and behaviours - direct and indirect hypnotic suggestion.

Direct and Indirect Hypnotic Suggestion

Direct suggestion is frequently used in hypnotherapy, as a way of influencing the behaviour of the mind. Making suggestions to somebody in the state of hypnosis, such as "You will not have back pain", or "You can now move freely" are certainly influential, but nowhere near as powerful as when we have distracted the mind away from being told what to do. If I were to tell you now, "Put this book down and do some stretching exercises," how would you feel? You may have a mixture of responses ranging from "Okay," to, "Do I have to?" to a simple, "No!" It all depends on how you react to direct suggestions, or commands, being given to you. At the very least you will think about whether you want to, or can carry out what is being suggested, or not.

If I said, however, "You know now that you have been reading lots of different exercises for your mind in the last few chapters, and you know how powerful it can be to think in different ways, and you've even imagined, just a moment ago, putting on a glove of anaesthesia. Well ... now we're getting onto the exciting part, so put this book down and begin by gently stretching out, and enjoying a feeling of freedom, and then I'll tell you the next amazing step which will gain you the ultimate relief!" Does this sound easier, more appealing, or more attractive? More than likely - as I distracted your attention away from what I wanted you to do, and gave you a compelling and exciting *reason* to do it. This we call an indirect suggestion. This is how the mind responds best. It needs, indeed craves, excitement to carry out suggested tasks or commands, or it questions them, and you question the motivation behind what you're being asked to do.

Step 6: Handing It Over to You

So, in this technique, the glove anaesthesia method (or GAM for short) we will include various direct and indirect suggestions to find ways of creating this imaginary glove of anaesthesia, which we can then use to get you the relief you want.

Using the GAM for the Ultimate Relief

So, here we go. You became accustomed in our earlier chapter to taking yourself into a light state of hypnosis, to open up the amazing power of your mind to make this process work in the best way for you. As a reminder, if you need to experience this again by *me* taking you into hypnosis then you can download your FREE MP3 audio recording at www.TomBarberMedia.com.

It's time now to follow these eight steps to make the GAM work for you.

1. *Send your hand away* – The GAM starts with you imagining your hand detaching from your body. Imagine your hand now separating from you, slowly moving it away from your arm and then floating it out in front of you. You might like to imagine it being suspended in front of you by

microscopic strands of translucent fibres barely visible to the human eye. Your hand can just rest there, floating and getting ready for step two.

2. *Imagine that hand becoming numb – (Indirect Suggestion)* – Now that hand is floating out in front of you, we are able to make it numb as we begin to mentally anaesthetise that hand. You can begin to imagine it perhaps being immersed in a bucket of ice and becoming numb like this, or you can imagine it like you've been to the dentist and the hand is becoming numb like your gums would after an injection, or where you've been laying on your arm or hand and it's become numb that way. Each person experiences this in different ways, so find the kind of numbness that works best for you, one which isn't unpleasant and that can remain in that hand as long as it needs to.

3. *Stroking numbness into the hand – (Direct Suggestion)* – Here we can now use some strong commands to increase the power of that numbness. Imagine that you can reach out and stroke an incredibly powerful dose of numbness into that hand. You might imagine that it's like watching a 3D movie and the hand has floated out of the T.V and is hovering in front of you (I'm reminded of the hero reaching out to touch the floating flowers in the film *Avatar*). You reach out now and stroke a numb sensation into that hand until you can imagine you have transferred more powerful mental anaesthesia completely into that hand. With each stroke the numbness becomes five times more potent than before. Then imagine that that totally

Step 6: Handing It Over to You

numb hand re-joins your arm and here you have your very own *glove of anaesthesia.*

4. *Test using the "pinch test"* - Now we need to test the mental numbness to make sure your hand feels no pain. It will possibly feel some *sensation,* but all messages of pain in that numb, anaesthetised hand are gone. So, now reach over with the hand that isn't mentally anesthetised and literally *pinch* the skin between your thumb and forefinger to see just how numb the hand is. If there is a sensation that is fine, but if it feels like pain when you pinch the skin, then follow step number 5. If there is no pain then proceed to step 7.

5. *Compound and numb further – (Indirect Suggestion) –* The great thing with this technique is that you can just keep going with it until you reach the desired state of numb mental anaesthesia that you need to. So to make the numbness even stronger now, lift your arm with the anesthetised hand on the end of it and slowly move it over to your other hand and then begin to transfer all of the numbness into your opposite hand, stroking it over there, like you are gently stroking a cat, just the way you started to in step 3. Keep stroking the numbness until it's all transferred over and then rest your hand back in its place. Now, do the same process again and transfer the numbness back into the original numb hand, with the glove of anaesthesia, stroking all the numbness back, this time finding that that original numb hand becomes ten or even twenty times more numb than before.

6. *Test again using the pinch test* - Once you have transferred the glove of anaesthesia back and forth between your hands a few times - each time the numbness increasing - then it's time to redo the pinch test by pinching that area of skin between your thumb and forefinger on the now mentally anaesthetised hand. When you feel nothing or simply just a sensation, but no pain at all, then we can successfully move onto the next step.

7. *Transferring the mental glove of anaesthesia to the pain area! – (Direct Suggestion)* – You have now created a powerful mental glove of anaesthesia and it's time to move it to the area of your back where it needs to be placed. Move your arm now to the part of your back where you want to place the numbness. Remember, the whole of your hand is carrying that mental anaesthesia, so you can place the back of your hand against your back. If the unwanted pain is in your shoulder area then you can place your hand palm down on the area. When it's where you need to place it, then begin to stroke all of the numbness out of your numb hand and into the back area where it needs to go. Keep stroking, and stroking, until all of the numbness is transferred over, and then rest your arm back in its place. Become aware now of how your back feels!

    Note: Don't worry if you can't reach the part of your back where you want to transfer the numbness to. In this case, simply place your hand on the opposite part of your chest, stomach or abdomen to where the pain in your back is. As you stroke the numbness into that area, imagine it seeping and permeating right the way through

Step 6: Handing It Over to You

your body to the part of your back that you want it
to.

8. *Return your hands to their normal state.* Now, before
we end, begin to imagine both of your hands
returning to complete normal feeling, whilst at the
same time your back retains all of the mental
anaesthesia and the numbness remains there.
Imagine all the blood running through the veins in
your hands, as all sensations return completely.

Keeping You Pain Free at Will!

There we have it, the GAM process in its entirety. How
does your back feel? As I said earlier, the great thing about
the GAM is that you can repeat it as many times as you
wish, and it can be a really powerful method of taking
control of pain and getting you to what this book is all
about … the Ultimate Relief. I have worked with hundreds
of people in my workshops using this method and many
report that it relieves them of their back pain for good, and
that just thinking about their own unique GAM process
brings them relief, but, if you need to, you can simply top
up the anaesthetised effect whenever you want. Just repeat
steps one to eight above.

Time to Rate It!

"Presently my rating of pain is _____."

Bonus Number 3!

I really love this technique, simply because I've seen such
amazingly dramatic results in so many people I have
worked with when using it. For my next Bonus Gift for

you I want to show you a live recorded GAM session I did with somebody suffering from wisdom tooth pain. It really shows you how you can simply go through this method and place the mental anaesthetised glove anywhere you need it to go. It's my next free gift to you! Go to www.TomBarberMedia.com and search for the "White Glove." Happy hunting!

Chapter 8
Step 7: Pain Still There!
What's Blocking You?

Have You Heard the Rumour? ... Your Mind and Body Are Connected!

In his well-known books on healing TMS (Tension Myositis Syndrome) and the mind-body connection, John Sarno (1984; 1991; 1998) reminds us of the long historical awareness and appreciation of the impact of emotions on the body. Hippocrates, as far back as 460 BCE – 370 BCE, wrote of the dangers to the human soul of being angry. The literature on the effect of emotion on bodily dis-ease is a very long one and way back in history gave people much more of an appreciation of themselves in a holistic sense. Holistic, sometimes misunderstood or dressed up as some kind of New Age approach, is certainly not a new term. It simply means taking the whole of the person into account. Before modern medicine, holistic was all that was available, and on the whole it worked quite well.

Then, the impact of the French philosopher and mathematician Rene Descartes's (1596-1650) ideas of dualism began to change this way of thinking, at least in the western world. Dualism is the idea that the mind and body are separate entities; this idea formed the very basis of the medical model, and this has lasted up to very recently in history. Whilst the medical model has of course done much to the health and longevity of the human race, in a way it stripped us of our innate appreciation that we are indeed holistic beings, with self-healing abilities.

In the last few years, the medical model's appreciation of mental health as an important part of the overall treatment of people has indeed started to become more appreciated, but consider the last time you went to your doctor.

Did the conversation sound like this?

You: "Doctor, I've this constant nagging pain in my upper back area."

Doctor: "Okay, tell me when it started and what was happening in your life at the time? Were you stressed? Did you experience the loss of somebody close to you, or the loss of anything else, and if so, how did you manage the emotions you felt at the time? Did you have support?"

Probably not. It is more likely that it went like this:

You: "Doctor, I've this constant nagging pain in my upper back area."

Doctor: "Okay, let's check what's happening."

This is then followed by your doctor checking your heartbeat, pulse, temperature and blood pressure. This isn't, of course, to say this physiological focus is wrong. It's

Step 7: Pain Still There!

important to have a thorough awareness of your body and the possible physical aspects of the pain, but so often this is where the medical model starts from, and finishes, treating your unique body as if it were exactly the same as any other body, which it is not. The psychological aspect of your pain is rarely given the attention it needs, and deserves.

The history of the mind-body connection is scattered with famous theorists, yet it's not the purpose of this book to delve deeply into the development of this area. During recent years, however, *Psychoneuroimmunology* (Ader, Cohen & Felten, 1981) or "PNI," the study of the interaction between psychological processes and the systems of the human body, is showing us links between the body's immune and nervous system and our mental health. The mind and body connecting scientifically, we might say.

Taking the principals of psychoneuroimmunology into a therapeutic intervention can be seen in our next approach to gaining you the Ultimate Relief to back pain - analytical hypnohealing, where we explore the pain in your body through the lens of its psychological and emotional roots.

Your Muscles Have Memory

When we practice something for long enough, like riding a bike, learning a dance routine, or tennis or golf shot, we create a lasting *muscle memory* that makes these newly learned actions automatic. This is how habits are formed. The downside to this muscle memory is that if we find ourselves in a situation of extreme anxiety or stress for even a short period of time, we can actually store this emotional experience away not just in our mind, but in our body also. Later on, when the original anxiety or stress provoking situation has passed, sometimes even years later, we are left with the body's physical memory of this emotional response, yet have lost the conscious memory of what was actually happening at that time. This makes it hard to make the connection between the original experience of pain and the accompanying bodily reaction to that original event, and what we are experiencing with pain today.

In our previous book, *Thinking Therapeutically: Hypnotic Skills and Strategies Explored* (2011) (which you can get at www.ThinkingTherapeutically.com), myself and Sandra Westland wrote a number of detailed accounts of our therapy sessions with clients presenting with varying problems such as driving test anxiety, phobias, low self-confidence, irritable bowel syndrome, weight loss and eating disorders, and low self-esteem.

One of my clients in the book, Antoine, complained of gagging every time he went to the dentist. Through taking him back through time using regression hypnosis, we saw how a simple and playful childhood event went distressingly wrong, with him ending up choking on his shirt collar, and how this event led to him choking in just the same way as an adult when anything came near his neck, and especially when he visited the dentist, which was his presenting problem. He didn't know the gagging was connected to this childhood event until we made the connection, and then it made perfect sense to him. Once this connection was made, and the emotion released, Antoine's gagging problem became a thing of the past.

Step 7: Pain Still There!

Looking Back ... The Analytical Healing Session

Having used many different methods of dealing with your back pain up to this point in this book, it's time now to look back at what may be "locking" the pain in your back in place. If you have not gained the ultimate relief from your back pain by now, then something is "stuck." Maybe your back is stuck in the past, and needs releasing. We have looked at how your body can store away aspects of your past traumatic experiences, and how these can lead to you experiencing back pain, born out of unfinished emotional or psychological business, and that's what we're going to address now: unfinished business.

We will create a link to the area of pain in your back, and then return to the time when the pain *first* occurred, where we can then explore the emotional and psychological connection between the physical pain in the now, and its origin. You might be very aware of when and where your back pain started, but simply *remembering* what was happening is not enough. The release of the stuck energy occurs through *re-experiencing* what happened at the time. We call this revivification. To do this will take seven steps.

To carry out this technique, we will be moving between the you of today, your current self, the person reading this book at the moment, and then the you that you were, back when the pain first appeared in your life. The easiest way to do this is to picture an image of you now. Perhaps you can imagine looking in the mirror and seeing yourself in the present. Have you got the image? When you have, then imagine another image of you, perhaps a photograph of you at some time in the past, when you were younger, and without back pain. Take some time now to get the images in your mind, as it's the movement between these two inner images of you that we are going to work with.

So, let's get going.

The 7-Step Analytical Healing Process

1. *Preparing your mind for discovery*

First we need to prepare your mind for unleashing its healing abilities, and to do this you can use the artfully vague method of relaxation you learnt in Chapter 6. Here it is again.

You're drifting to a different place now, somewhere perhaps far away. Wherever you find yourself drifting to in your mind, it's simply a place where you can imagine completely and utterly switching off and relaxing very deeply. It may be somewhere that you've visited before in the past, or it could be somewhere you're planning to go to, or somewhere you'd really like to be, anywhere in the world. It could even be a place in your imagination. The only thing that matters is that in your place you can just simply let go, switch off and relax completely.

Step 7: Pain Still There!

Nobody wants anything from you there or expects anything from you, and the only thing there is for you to do is relax deeply and soundly. When you are in that place, wherever it may be, then you can begin to bring it alive and make it real, as if you've been magically transported right back into that memory, or that experience, as if you are actually there, and begin to notice what you see around you, what different sights appear to you ... and then notice what sounds you begin to hear, and where those sounds are coming from.

It may even just be the sound of silence. And then you begin to notice the thoughts that drift through your mind there, and also you get a sense of how you feel in that place, both in your body and mind. In this place you can feel as completely relaxed as you ever have anywhere before. It's a special place of calm, peace and tranquillity, your special place and you can just stay there and experience it, and let yourself be ...

Now we can move on to the first linking procedure. You can simply take each step one at a time.

2.   *Directing your attention to the area of pain*

Now we can begin to go to the pain area, our first point. You don't need to repeat this to yourself, just follow the directions.

I want you to imagine turning your eyes inwards, and allow yourself to move inside your body, right down through your body to the area of pain. When you arrive that point, I want you to now describe what you have there.

Complete the following descriptions:

Its colour is _____.
Its shape is _____.
Its temperature is _____.
Its sound is _____.
Its feeling is _____.

When you have a description, then we have contextualised your bodily pain in your mind and are ready to make the link. Keep the description in your mind while we move on to step 3.

3. *Making the link*

The next part in this process is what will make the link between the pain and the psychological reason for the pain remaining in your body. Read the following sentence until you are familiar with it and can then say it with your eyes closed.

> "I am going to count to three and then I will be transported back to just a few moments before my back pain *first* appeared in my life (1-2-3)."

When you've done this, then the next step is to establish the scene so we can unearth what's happening there.

4. *Establishing the scene*

To do this, complete the following clarifying questions:

> Are you inside or outside? _____.
> Is it daytime or evening? _____.
> Are you alone or is there somebody there with you? _____.
> How old are you? _____.

Step 7: Pain Still There!

What is happening? _____.

Now, let's go deeper into this place. Really be in this experience *as the younger you*, and complete the following sentences:

I feel _____.
I wish _____.
I must _____.
I secretly _____.
I need _____.
I want _____.
I will _____.
Please _____.

Establish as accurate a picture as possible with as many details and feelings as become apparent to you. Allow the experience to unfold.

5. *Starting the healing*

The next step is to inform this image of you from the past as to what they need to know now to let the pain go. So, imagine you become your present-day self again, and as you look at your younger self where this pain first started, you are the only person in the whole world that knows how this younger you feels ... You are the only person in the whole world that knows how this event has affected your younger self ... You are the only person that knows what that younger you needs to hear ... And you are the only person that knows the nurturing, comforting and reassurance this younger you needs. So, what would you like to say and do now for that younger you? What words of support or encouragement does that younger you need to hear? Do they need a hug or a reassuring touch?

Take a few moments to say it out loud, and offer what is needed.

6.   *The integration*

Imagine now that you become the younger you, having heard what the present day you has just said. I wonder if there's anything you would like to say back? If so, take a few moments to say it now. Then imagine moving back into your present-day self. What's it like to hear your younger self say that? Is there anything more you'd like to say now to help that younger you let go of the pain? If so, take a few moments to say that now. If not, then you might want to give the younger you a hug or hold your younger self … and as you do … that younger self becomes part of you and integrates deep within you.

From now on you know that whenever you have those feelings of pain, your younger self is re-experiencing that time in your life … And so you can always go inside your mind like this and tell that part of you what they need to hear, or just listen to them … and maybe give them a hug or some reassurance … or whatever they need at that time.

7.   *Checking the physical symptoms*

Now, I want you once again to go back inside your body to that area in your back you described earlier, and then describe what you have there now. Notice any changes and complete the following sentences:

Its colour is _____.
Its shape is _____.
Its temperature is _____.

Step 7: Pain Still There!

Its sound is _____.

Its feeling is _____.

There you have it: one of the most powerful techniques I've used for dealing with back pain. In my workshops (you can find your nearest workshop location at www.TheBookOnBackPainWorkshop.com) we go a lot further with the dialogue between your current self and the you of the past, where the pain started, and get some quite startling results, but many people have gained incredible relief from simply going through this 7-step process just as it is here. It can be important to revisit this technique periodically, as each time you do, you can unblock and release potentially stored up emotion of the past. Once you've then processed this and made sense of it, going back and experiencing the technique again can unearth what else might be there. It becomes a journey of self-discovery.

Time to Rate It!

"Presently my rating of pain is _____."

Remember, practicing as much as possible gets you accustomed to linking the physical and psychological aspects of your pain, and thus helps you take control of the whole of you. Practice, practice, and practice some more.

Chapter 9
Step 8: Emotional Freedom Technique
The Final Frontier of Ultimate Relief

Emotional Freedom Technique

The Emotional Freedom Technique, or EFT for short, is a method of "clearing" emotional and physical imbalances by combining the power of (hypnotic) suggestion and meridian energy techniques. EFT was developed by Gary Craig in the early 1990's, and uses the major meridian channels and governing vessels found in Chinese medicine. The meridian channels are like an energy highway in the human body. According to Chinese medicine, Qi (or chi, pronounced "chee") energy flows through the meridian highway, accessing all parts of the body, and these meridians can be mapped throughout your body. It has been found that by tapping on these meridian energy points (the spots on the diagram below – see *figure 9:1*) while directing your attention on the problem at hand, in your case back pain, a release of energy takes place and the physical pain is eased. EFT holds the premise that all negative emotion is a disruption in the body's energy system and by bringing harmony back to the system, a healthy balance between mind and body can be restored.

Figure 9:1 EFT Face and Body Points

What Gets Your Back Up?

Have you ever described somebody as a "pain in the neck" or maybe you "just can't stomach" a situation any longer? The language you use powerfully communicates both an explicit message, and also what you are *not* saying, with conscious awareness. The phrases you find yourself using, such as "You get my back up," can be a meaningful expression of what's really happening within you, at a deeper level, and especially within your body. If you think now about the kinds of phrases you use in your everyday conversations, how many of them include the words "back" and "pain?" As Sue Knight writes in *NLP at Work: The Essence of Excellence* (2009), "Your language is an embroidery of patterns of words that tell your story." (p. 65)

Step 8: Emotional Freedom Technique

Louise Hay, in her international bestselling book, *You Can Heal Your Life* (2004) - which you can get at www.TomBarberMedia.com - details exquisitely how our body can experience dis-ease stemming from our mind. Hay describes, for example, how our back problems can echo a problem with the support we experience in our life. She offers an affirmation to counteract the currently held thought pattern perpetuating the back problem, such as "I know life always supports me." (p. 151)

More Specific Areas of Back Pain

Hay specifically divides the back into three areas: the lower, middle and upper back, and suggests the probable thoughts or belief pattern's that are the cause of the problem in these specific regions. (p. 152)

- For the lower back, she suggests "Fear of money. Lack of financial support."
- For the middle back, "Guilt. Stuck in all that *stuff* back there. Get off my back."
- And for the upper back, "Lack of emotional support. Feeling unloved. Holding back love."

Where in your back do you experience pain or problems? Can you see a link between these regions and what Louise Hay is suggesting? It may have no meaning for you immediately, but if you look back to the time when your back pain started, can you perhaps see any connection or correlation then to what she is suggesting as the psychological reason for the pain or problem? I have experienced some very surprising reactions to these suggested causes from people I have worked with in the past. If they were not experiencing the problematic belief Hay suggests in their life at that time, they were certainly able to trace the roots of their pain back to a time where these suggested thoughts and beliefs made total sense to them. It becomes clear for many people, through Hay's suggestions, that there is more to back pain than just the physical experience.

Whether you believe that the body can literally speak for the mind or not, let's try something. I want you to think of a person or situation that is now causing or has in the past caused you anxiety or distress. It could be a situation at work with a boss or colleague, a difficulty at home with a family member or partner, or perhaps a friend is upsetting you.

Complete the blanks in these sentences. When you do this exercise, remember: you're not going to have to tell anyone about it or show it to anybody. Be as frank as you can and let your emotions rule for the time being ... Let rip! Go for it! Don't hold back!

This situation is a _____.
This person is/has really _____.
I'm really _____ of all this.
I am _____ of this person/situation.
I feel _____ by this person/situation.

Do you notice any similarities between your language and your physical experience? It isn't always the case every time I work with clients suffering from back pain, but the number of times I hear them use terms such as, "I have to watch my back around that person," or "That person is really getting my back up," is surprisingly high.

Other phrases that I've heard clients use include:

Step 8: Emotional Freedom Technique

"They stab me in the back."
"I wish they would just back off."
"They're on my back the whole time."
"I wish I could just put things back to how they were."
"I just wish he/she would come back."
"It's back-breaking work."

And other not so obvious phrases such as:

"It feels like a lead weight I carry around all the time."
"It's all on my shoulders."
"I shoulder all of it."
"It's a heavy burden."
"It weighs me down."

I could list many more, but I think you get the gist. Many of these phrases directly relate to the back area, or describe a heavy burden being placed on somebody. When I've explored the way people describe difficult or ongoing situations in their life and then look at the link, the commonalities can lead us to what really needs to be explored.

The Ultimate Clearing for Long Lasting Relief

So, now we have you thinking about your inner self-talk and the phrases you use, which could have been reinforcing your back pain in some way, let's look at what kind of vocabulary you can benefit from, from now on, as this will form the powerful foundations for your future ultimate relief.

Using Louise Hay's examples from earlier as a guide, let's look at her suggested probable causes for each area of the back that encounters problems, and the affirmations for the three different regions she suggests. (p. 152)

- Lower back - "Fear of money. Lack of financial support."

As a positive change affirmation, Hay suggests, "I trust the process of life. All I need is always taken care of. I am safe."

- Middle back - "Guilt. Stuck in all that *stuff* back there. Get off my back."

Hay's suggested affirmation: "I release the past. I am free to move forward with love in my heart."

- Upper back - "Lack of emotional support. Feeling unloved. Holding back love."

Suggested affirmation: "I love and approve of myself. Life supports and loves me."

Choose which affirmation is appropriate for you now. You don't have to agree with it completely, but it will give you a start. The next step is to create your own personalised statement, which we will use during the clearing process, as we rid you of the negative connections between your mind and your back pain. This will be a combination of what EFT calls the "set up statement," followed by the relevant affirmation from above, for you.

EFT Step 1 - The Set Up Statement

In the Emotional Freedom Technique, the "set up statement" is the affirmation that will connect the physical part of the process, the tapping procedure, with your mind. The set up statement will be relative to where your back pain is: lower, middle or upper regions. If you experience your back pain moving, we will look at how to apply the set up statement appropriately to that also.

So, the set up statement will always begin: "Even though I have this lower/middle/upper (choose) back pain, I completely love and approve of myself."

Here you have your basic set up statement. Say it to yourself now and get a feel for how it sits with you.

"Even though I have this lower/middle/upper (choose) back pain, I completely love and approve of myself."

How does it sound? A little simplistic? Are you unsure as to whether you love and approve of yourself? Well, it's important at this stage not to question this part of the process too much. All you need to do is to begin to create your personal set up statement. Go with it for now and you'll see what I mean. The end result, relief from the pain, is what matters.

We're going to extend it now and make it personal for you. Here is the first part of the statement again.

"Even though I have this lower/middle/upper (choose) back pain, I completely love and approve of myself."

Now we're going to add one of the statements from Louise Hay's affirmations above, relative to where you are experience the pain, so choose one of the following statements:

- Lower back - "I trust the process of life. All I need is always taken care of. I am safe."
- Middle back - "I release the past. I am free to move forward with love in my heart."
- Upper back - "I love and approve of myself. Life supports and loves me."

So, if you experience pain in your lower back, your set up statement will go as follows:

"Even though I have this lower back pain, I completely love and approve of myself. I trust the process of life. All I need is always taken care of. I am safe."

For middle back pain:

"Even though I have this middle back pain, I completely love and approve of myself. I release the past. I am free to move forward with love in my heart."

And for upper back pain:

"Even though I have this upper back pain, I completely love and approve of myself. I love and approve of myself. Life supports and loves me."

Here is the first part of your EFT process, the set up statement, completed. You have your own personalised statement and affirmation to use with the next part of the technique, and this will become a powerful mantra for you in getting the ultimate relief.

I said earlier that you may experience your back pain in different places. Often, pain can move around. If this is the case, I suggest playing around with the affirmation statements, so that you find one that fits for you. It may be a combination of all three as follows:

"Even though I have this back pain, I completely love and approve of myself. I trust life, release the past, and I am free and supported."

EFT Step 2 - Tapping - The Pain-Taking Process

Tapping is a simple but effective technique that engages the body in the state of hypnosis and then uses acupressure to release trapped energy. This form of psychological acupressure is based on the same energy meridians used in traditional acupuncture to treat physical ailments for over five thousand years. Tapping works to clear the emotional block from your body's bioenergy system, thus restoring your mind-body balance.

To start, let's first rate the current intensity of pain in your back. We will use faces scale from Chapter 1. This will give us an indication as to success of the tapping process as we go through it. Rate your pain now.

0	1	2	3	4	5
No Hurt	Hurts Little Bit	Hurts Little More	Hurts Even More	Hurts Whole Lot	Hurts Worst

EFT Face and Body Points

Now we have a starting place, we can begin the tapping process in conjunction with saying the unique set up statement you have created. The points we are going to tap are as follows, starting from the top of the diagram and working down.

Figure 9:2 EFT Face and Body Points Descriptions – From Right to Left

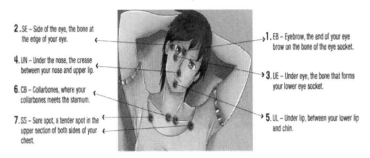

2. SE – Side of the eye, the bone at the edge of your eye.

4. UN – Under the nose, the crease between your nose and upper lip.

6. CB – Collarbones, where your collarbones meets the sternum.

7. SS – Sore spot, a tender spot in the upper section of both sides of your chest.

1. EB – Eyebrow, the end of your eye brow on the bone of the eye socket.

3. UE – Under eye, the bone that forms your lower eye socket.

5. UL – Under lip, between your lower lip and chin.

The Tapping Procedure

Let's use middle back pain as an example. Change the statements to suit you.

1. To start, say your set up statement three times out loud, so for middle back pain you would say out loud:

   "Even though I have this middle back pain, I completely love and approve of myself. I release the past. I am free to move forward with love in my heart."

   Choose your set up statement from earlier and say it out loud three times now. Whilst you say it, gently rub the sore spot. It doesn't matter if you rub on the left or right side of your chest.

2. Next, start the tapping process, beginning at your eyebrow point. Refer to the diagram above to

remind you. You need to tap this area with the tips of two or three fingers for a total of seven times, while at the same time saying your personalised statement.

3. Move from your eyebrow to the side of your eye and again tap that spot seven times while repeating your set up statement. Do the same for under the eye, under the nose, under the lip and your collar bone, each time tapping while saying your statement.

4. Once you have completed the process, then go back to your intensity rating and give it a score. We want the rating of pain to move down in its intensity, but just one tapping session may not be enough, so if you score the intensity of your back pain just one point less than it was, that's okay. We will work down gradually.

5. Now repeat steps 1 to 4 above again, until you've reached zero on the intensity scale, or as low as you can go in this session.

Further Sessions

Each time you use the EFT method in future sessions, you might like to adapt your set up statement to be more specific. As you may know, when you get relief in one area of your back, you may feel it in another place, so play around with the set up statements until you find what works for you. Try doing it at different times of the day and in different locations so you change the "state" you are working in.

There is so much more to EFT that can make this process even more powerful. You've made a great start at unblocking your energy highways and using your personal affirmation, which will together enable you to feel greater relief from pain. To find out how you can add to your knowledge of EFT, go to www.TomBarberMedia.com and click on the link to *EFT Therapy's* free manual and guide.

This time, we're going to rate your back pain intensity in the next chapter.

Chapter 10
Conclusion
FeedBACK

There's No Failure, Only Feedback

So we are at our final chapter. At this stage I really want to know more about how you have got on with the methods and techniques you have learned. Go again now to www.TheBookOnBackPainFeedback.com and update me on what's really helped you and how you're using the book to get the ultimate relief from pain. Remember that from the feedback page you can also find out about others' experiences through my social media pages and get the additional bonus of learning from them how they have adapted and perfected these techniques so you can really get creative and do the same.

Time to Rate It!

What's the intensity rating of your back now? Look back at Chapter 1 and the rating you gave yourself and notice what's happened. Tracking your progress really is the key to getting the changes you want. Only when you keep checking the outcome of the techniques you are using, will you find what really works for you.

The people I help in my workshops and private sessions all respond differently to each of the methods they learn. Some will find the mindfulness exercises incredibly helpful, whereas others find EFT the most transformational. The trick is to get as good at using as many of these methods as you can. It's likely you've suffered from pain for some time, so there's no rush. Take your time and master each technique.

Mastery of Your Mind - Bonus Gift Number 4

I hope in this book you have got a deeper understanding as to the many ways you can use your infinitely powerful mind to take charge of your physical experience and ultimately your life. Now I'm going to tell you about a *massive* bonus I have for you. I'm inviting you to London to spend two whole days with me learning about hypnosis and NLP, for free! Yes, entirely free! People travel from many different countries to attend these two days of free training, and I want to give you a place as a thank you for reading this book and trying the methods I've been teaching you. There's so much more to learn about how you can use your mind for creative change, and, as it's my passion to help as many people as possible take charge in their lives, I want to share with you some incredibly powerful secrets about how your mind works and how you can completely change the way you communicate with others and yourself.

In our two days together, you will learn about the different states of hypnotic trance, brain states and frequencies, and biofeedback methods. You'll learn various ways of achieving the hypnotic trance states, safely and effectively. We will also explore the powerful use of suggestion and how you can access your deep inner mind through using imagery techniques. Along with myself and Sandra Westland (author of *Smashing the Glass Ceiling: The Ultimate Women's Guide to Business Success* – www.SmashingTheGlassCeiling.com) we will also explore how you can further use NLP, which has been described by *Psychology Today* magazine as "the most powerful vehicle for change in the 21st century." and by *Time* magazine as "one of the biggest breakthroughs in the technology of achievement and human excellence." You'll learn the fundamentals of how human beings operate so you can fine tune how to do *anything* successfully. You'll also learn more about the sensory modalities I've written about in this book and about the deeper structure of language and how changing just a few things in your own language patterns can make amazing differences in your life.

To get your free ticket to attend these packed two days of certified training for absolutely free, simply go to www.FreeHypnosisAndNLPCourse.co.uk. You will see when the next course is running and can book your place immediately online.

Why would you want to learn more about your mind to help you with back pain? Well, I've seen over the years many hundreds of people who, once they understand themselves, others and the world better, experience a massive change in how their body responds to stressful or anxiety-provoking situations. Looking after your mental muscles is just as important as looking after your body.

Keeping It Going

You now have eight different ways you can practice daily to fine tune your mind into getting you the ultimate relief. The best way I've found my students maintaining their use of these techniques is to make them part of their daily routine, like taking a shower or brushing your teeth. Most of the techniques are very quick to use, so how about committing to a time in your day *now* where you'll integrate them into your life. Make a decision *now* as to when that's going to be, and stick by it.

The Ultimate Relief Bootcamp

During the many years I have been teaching my Ultimate Relief programme, I've met so many people that have mastered the methods you've learned in this book as well as the many other approaches I teach on my workshops. They have literally changed their lives. To experience these methods along with other people in an experiential way makes a remarkable difference in how you understand and implement them at a deeper personal level, which is why I want to tell you now about my totally new Ultimate Relief Bootcamp, which has been the culmination of many years of success on my workshops across the world in finding out what really works and fine tuning these methods, and many others, that you can learn to add to your personal ultimate relief programme. I've launched my Bootcamp to take you through what would ordinarily take months of work to achieve, but in the Bootcamp you will master your mind and your body to take control of your life. In these two days you will learn many other incredibly powerful methods and techniques that I simply haven't been able to cram into this book, but which will help you take the ultimate control of your back pain, your body, your mind

Conclusion

and ultimately your life to an entirely new level. No matter where you are in the world, I aim to bring the Ultimate Relief Bootcamp to you. It's my passion, my own personal well-formed outcome, if you like. You can find out more about when and where your nearest Bootcamp is and book your place at www.UltimateReliefBootCamp.com.

I hope to see you there and I hope this book has transformed your relationship with your body, and your belief in the power of your mind, as much as I wanted it to.

Resources

www.TheBookOnBackPain.co.uk – Order further copies of *The Book on Back Pain*.

www.TheBookOnBackPainWorkshop.com – Find out when and where Tom's Back Pain Workshop programme is coming to you.

www.UltimateReliefBootCamp.com – Join Tom and others for two days of powerful, inspirational, life-changing and transformational change. The Ultimate Relief from back pain happens here!

www.TheBookOnBackPainFeedback.com – Leave Tom feedback on how you have used his Ultimate Relief methods and join *The Book on Back Pain* social media sites to hear how others have mastered these too.

www.TomBarberMedia.com – Get help and resources written about in this book.

www.ThinkingTherapeutically.com – Tom Barber and Sandra Westland's highly acclaimed book on hypnotherapy, NLP and imagery.

www.ContemporaryCollege.com – UK certified training in hypnosis, hypnotherapy, NLP, counselling and psychotherapy.

www.FreeHypnosisAndNLPCourse.co.uk – Your bonus free course in hypnosis and NLP skills.

www.WriteYourUltimateBook.com – Explore Raymond Aaron's amazing 10-10-10 program.

www.SmashingTheGlassCeiling.com – Sandra Westland's book on women and business success.

www.TomBarber.co.uk – Tom's personal therapy website.

References

Ader, R., Cohen, N., & Felten, D. (1991) *Psychoneuroimmunology*. (2nd Edition) London: Academic Press.

Barber, T. & Westland, S. (2011) *Thinking Therapeutically: Hypnotic Skills and Strategies Explored*. Carmarthen: Crown House Publishing.

Bodenhamer, B. & Hall, L. (2001) *The User's Manual for the Brain*: Volume 1. Carmarthen: Crown House Publishing.

Craig, G. (2011) *The Eft Manual: Everyday Eft: Emotional Freedom Techniques*. CA: Energy Psychology Press.

Fisher, M. (2012) *Mindfulness and the Art of Managing Anger*. East Sussex: Leaping Hare Press.

Germer, C. *et al* (2005) *Mindfulness and Psychotherapy*. London: Guilford Press.

Hay, L. (2004) *You Can Heal Your Life*. London: Hay House UK.

Hockenberry, M. & Wilson, D. (2013) *Wong's Essentials of Pediatric Nursing, 9th Edition*. Missouri: Elsevier Mosby.

Holger, C. (2012) Mindfulness-based stress reduction for low back pain. A systematic review. *BMC Complementary and Alternative Medicine*, 12:162. doi:10.1186/1472-6882-12-162.

Knight, S. (2009) *NLP at Work: The Essence of Excellence*. London: Nicholas Brealey Publishing.

McCaffery M. & Pasero C. (1999) *Pain: Clinical Manual*. St. Louis: Mosby Inc.

Melzack, R. & Wall, P. (1965) Pain Mechanisms: A New Theory. *Science, New Series*, 150, 3699: 971-979.

Miller, G.A., Galanter, E., & Pribram, K.A. (1960) *Plans and the Structure of Behavior*. New York: Holt, Rhinehart, & Winston.

Sarno, J. E. (1991) *Healing Back Pain: the Mind-Body Connection*. New York: Warner Books.

Segal, Z. *et al.* (2010) *Mindfulness for Pain Relief: Guided Practices for Reclaiming Your Body and Your Life*. CO: Sounds True Inc.

Shapiro, S. & Carlson, L. (Authors) (2009) *The Art and Science of Mindfulness: Integrating Mindfulness into Psychology and the Helping Professions*. DC: American Psychological Association.

Siegel, D. J. (2007) "Mindfulness training and neural integration: Differentiation of distinct streams of awareness and the cultivation of well-being." *Social Cognitive and Affective Neuroscience*. 2 (4): 259–63. doi:10.1093/scan/nsm034. PMC 2566758.

Wynne, A. (2007) *The Origin of Buddhist Mediation*. London: Routledge.

Zautra, A., Fasman, R., Davis, M., & Craig, A. (2010) The effects of slow breathing on affective responses to pain

stimuli: An experimental study. *Pain.* 149 (1), 12-18
DOI:10.1016/j.pain.2009.10.001

Index

affirmation 99, 102, 104
amygdala 6
anaesthesia.................................... 79, 80, 81, 82, 83
anger..9, 16
anterior cingulate cortex 6
anxiety 3, 6, 9, 16, 67, 73, 87, 88, 100, 111
arthritis...29, 30
Auditory-Visual-Auditory Digital-Kinaesthetic-
   Olfactory-Gustatory (AVADKOG) 51, 52, 59
back
   lower.............................. 1, 3, 16, 73, 99, 102, 104
   middle.................................. 73, 99, 102, 104, 106
   upper..................................... 73, 86, 99, 102, 104
Bodenhammer, Bob..31
brain...6, 10, 11, 110
breathing..................................... 16, 18, 20, 25, 26, 67, 71, 74
Buddha...15, 16
Carlson, Linda..16
Chief Executive Officer (CEO) 73, 75
chiropractor 2, 3
Craig, Gary 97
Cramer, Holger 16
depression...6, 16
Descartes, Rene 85
Dilts, Robert..39
dorsal horn 10, 11
Emotional Freedom Technique (EFT).xiii, 97, 98, 102, 104,
   105, 106, 107, 110
enlightenment 15
Erickson, Milton...68
exercises 16, 17, 78, 110

121

fear... 3, 9

Fisher, Mike.. 16, 117

Galanter, Eugene... 39

gate control (theory of pain).............................. 10

Germer, Christopher.. 16

Glove Anaesthesia Method (GAM)..................... 77

Hay, Louise........................... 99, 100, 101, 102, 103

Hippocrates... 85

hypnosis.................11, 12, 64, 65, 69, 79, 88, 105, 110, 115

hypnotherapy............................... 24, 68, 78, 115

Kabat-Zinn, Jon... 16

Master Control Room.............. 63, 65, 67, 70, 72, 73, 74

medication.. 17, 23

Melzack, Ronald...................................xiii, 10, 11

meridian channels.. 97

Miller, George.. 39

mind ... ix, xv, 3, 5, 6, 12, 13, 16, 18, 19, 23, 25, 31, 41, 42, 43, 44, 45, 46, 48, 49, 52, 54, 55, 65, 66, 67, 69, 70, 71, 72, 73, 74, 75, 78, 79, 85, 86, 87, 90, 91, 92, 98, 100, 102, 103, 105, 110, 111, 112, 113

    base subconscious 42

    conscious 42, 43

    intermediate subconscious........................... 42

    subconscious .30, 42, 43, 44, 45, 46, 49, 64, 65, 67, 71, 72, 73

mindfulness..................15, 16, 17, 18, 21, 23, 26, 110

modalities (sensory)............................. 54, 59, 111

    auditory 52, 55, 56, 59

    auditory digital....................................... 52, 59

    gustatory... 52, 59

    kinaesthetic............................... 52, 55, 56, 59

    olfactory.. 52, 59

    visual... 52, 55, 56, 59

    muscle memory 87

Neuro Linguistic Programming (NLP) .. 12, 31, 40, 51, 52, 110, 111, 115
pain
    acute 9
    chronic..6, 10
    emotional 3, 6, 8, 9, 87, 88, 89, 97, 99, 102, 105
    physical .. xv, 6, 9, 72, 87, 88, 89, 94, 95, 97, 100, 102, 105, 110
pathway, emotional...6
pathway, sensory...6
Pavlov, Ivan...19
Ponty, Maurice Merleau 25
Pribram, Karl...39
psychoneuroimmunology (PNI) 87
Rubin, Edgar 22
Sarno, John...17, 85
self-image..7
self-speak 59
Shapiro, Shauna 16
Siegel, Dan...16
spinal cord 10, 11
spinothalamic tract..11
stress.. 3, 7, 65, 67, 74, 87
submodalities (sensory)...54, 58
suggestion
    direct...78, 80, 82
    indirect 78
tapping 97, 105, 106, 107
Tension Myosistis Syndrome (TMS) 85
Test Operation Test Exit (TOTE) 38, 39, 40, 61
Ultimate Reliefxi, 1, 3, 23, 55, 70, 72, 79, 83, 87, 89, 97, 104, 112, 115
Well Formed Outcome (WFO)..31
Westland, Sandra................................... ix, 88, 111, 115, 116

Wynne, Alexander 16
Zautra, Alex 16

[handwritten notes]

Self Hypnos Website   P 12

Relax Voice 2 Faces   P 22

anthpnos Website   P 24

Website Hypnos N.L.P.   P 40

N L P → AVADKOG   P 32

be all you can be

TRAINING IN

HYPNOTHERAPY
•
PSYCHOTHERAPY
•
COUNSELLING
•
NLP

www.ContemporaryCollege.com

Made in the USA
Charleston, SC
30 August 2013